GCSE AQA A
Core Science
Foundation — the Basics
The Workbook

This book is for anyone doing **GCSE AQA A Core Science** at foundation level, with a predicted grade of D or below.
(If you're not sure what your predicted grade is, your teacher will be able to tell you.)

It's full of **useful practice questions** to help you **get to grips with** the essential science you'll need for the exams.

And of course, there are some daft bits to make the whole thing vaguely entertaining for you.

What CGP is all about

Our sole aim here at CGP is to produce the highest quality books — carefully written, immaculately presented and dangerously close to being funny.

Then we work our socks off to get them out to you — at the cheapest possible prices.

Contents

Biology 1a — Human Biology

Biology 1b — Environment and Evolution

Chemistry 1a — Products from Rocks

Chemistry 1b — Oils, Earth and Atmosphere

Physics 1a — Energy

Physics 1b — Electricity and Waves

Published by CGP

Editors:
Katherine Craig, Emma Elder, Felicity Inkpen, Helen Ronan, Jane Sawers, Jane Towle, Dawn Wright.

Contributors:
Paddy Gannon.

ISBN: 978 1 84762 711 7

With thanks to Glenn Rogers and Hayley Thompson for the proofreading.

With thanks to Jeremy Cooper, Janet Cruse-Sawyer and Ian Francis for the reviewing.

With thanks to Jan Greenway, Laura Jakubowski and Laura Stoney for the copyright research.

Graph of sulfur dioxide on page 29, source ww2.defra.gov.uk © Crown copyright reproduced under the terms of the Click-Use licence.

Every effort has been made to locate copyright holders and obtain permission to reproduce sources. For those sources where it has been difficult to trace the originator of the work, we would be grateful for information. If any copyright holder would like us to make an amendment to the acknowledgements, please notify us and we will gladly update the book at the next reprint. Thank you.

www.cgpbooks.co.uk

Printed by Elanders Ltd, Newcastle upon Tyne.
Clipart from Corel®
Based on the classic CGP style created by Richard Parsons.

Diet and Metabolic Rate

Q1 What is a **healthy diet**? Tick the right box.

- ☐ A diet that gives you no energy but the right amount of different foods.
- ☐ A diet that gives you more energy than you need and a few different foods.
- ☐ A diet that gives you the energy you need and the right amount of different foods.

Q2 Use the words in the box to fill in the gaps in the sentences.

warm	minerals	energy	cells	energy

a) Protein is needed to build ....

b) Carbohydrates give you ....

c) Fats are needed to keep .... They also give ....

d) Vitamins and .... are needed to stay healthy.

Q3 a) What is your metabolism? Circle the answer.

all the muscles in your body — all the proteins in your body — all the chemical reactions in your body

b) What is your metabolic rate? Circle the answer.

how fast your muscles grow — the speed proteins are used to build cells in your body — the speed of chemical reactions in your body

Q4 Do these people have a **fast** or a **slow metabolic rate**? Tick the right boxes.

	Fast metabolic rate	Slow metabolic rate
a) Steven doesn't have much muscle.	☐	☐
b) Emily has an active job.	☐	☐
c) David does lots of exercise.	☐	☐

Being Healthy

Q1 a) What is an **unbalanced diet**? Tick **two** boxes.

- [ ] It's where people eat too much.
- [ ] It's where people eat more vegetables than meat.
- [ ] It's where people eat too little.
- [ ] It's where people eat food that gives them all the energy they need.

b) Circle the right word to complete the sentence.

Eating too much can make a person overweight or **underweight** / **obese**.

c) Draw lines to complete the sentences. One has been done for you.

Someone who is malnourished...	... doesn't eat enough vitamins or minerals.
Someone who has a deficiency disease...	... can't control the level of sugar in their blood.
Someone who has type 2 diabetes...	... eats an unbalanced diet.

Q2 Paula **exercises** every day. Michael does no exercise.

a) Who is probably healthier, Paula or Michael?

....

b) Paula has a slow metabolic rate. What could have caused this?
Circle the answer.

her genes **eating too many vitamins** **having diabetes** **eating too much protein**

Q3 a) What is **cholesterol**? Circle your answer.

a type of exercise **a mineral** **a type of fat found in your body** **a diet**

b) Circle the right words in the sentences below.

Some people have too much cholesterol because of their **genes** / **metabolic rate**.

People with too much cholesterol might get **a deficiency disease** / **heart disease**.

Losing Weight

Q1 a) What does your **weight** depend on? Circle **two** answers.

how often you eat Brussels sprouts | how much energy you take in | whether you're allergic to nuts | how much energy you use

b) Circle the right words in the sentences below.

When you eat you **take in** / **use** energy.

When you exercise you **take in** / **use** energy.

c) What do you need to do to lose weight? Circle the answer.

Take in more energy than you use. | Take in less energy than you use.

Q2 Look at the two **studies** about losing weight below.

Study A	Study B
Claim: A cereal helps you lose weight	**Claim**: A drug helps you lose weight
Report by: Girl band Kandyfloss	**Report by**: Professor Large
Study based on: 4 people	**Study based on**: 6000 people
Number of other studies with the same result: 0	**Number of other studies with the same result**: 10

a) What things make a study more reliable? Tick **three** answers.

- The report is written by a real scientist. ☐
- The report is written by a girl band. ☐
- The study asks lots of people. ☐
- Other studies find the same result. ☐

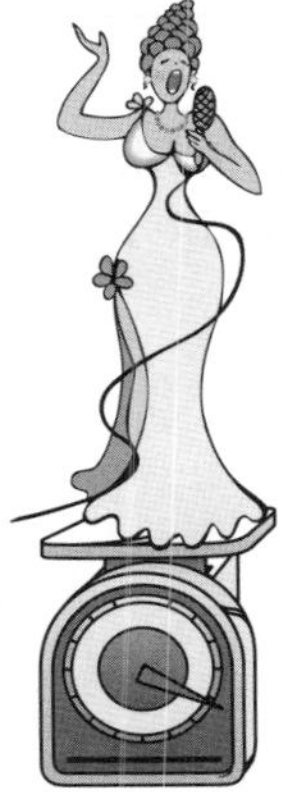

b) Which claim is more likely to be true? Circle the answer.

The claim in study A. | **The claim in study B.**

Fighting Disease

Q1 Complete the sentence by using the right word underneath.

Microorganisms that cause infectious diseases are called ....

pathogens **antibodies**

Q2 What **stops microorganisms** getting into your body? Circle **three** answers.

Antibodies **Make up** **Scabs** **Hair and mucus in your nose** **Tattoos** **Skin**

Q3 Circle the right words to complete the sentences.

Bacteria copy themselves very quickly inside your **hair / body**. They make you feel ill by **damaging your cells / forming scabs**. They also make you feel ill by making **toxins / mucus**. Viruses copy themselves very quickly inside your **scabs / cells**. They make you feel ill by **damaging your cells / forming scabs**.

Q4 a) How do **white blood cells** protect your body from infection? Circle **two** answers.

ingest pathogens **make antibodies** **make red blood cells** **ingest antibodies**

b) White blood cells also make antitoxins. How do antitoxins protect you from diseases? Tick the right box.

- They poison red blood cells. ☐
- They stop antibodies made by bacteria. ☐
- They poison bacteria. ☐
- They stop toxins made by bacteria. ☐

Vaccines

Q1 What is a **vaccine**? Circle the answer.

An injection of living pathogens.

An injection of antibodies.

An injection of white blood cells.

An injection of dead or inactive pathogens.

Q2 Are the sentences **true** or **false**? Tick the right boxes.

		True	False
a)	Vaccines contain pathogens that can kill you.	☐	☐
b)	White blood cells make antibiotics to kill pathogens in vaccines.	☐	☐
c)	Vaccines make you immune to a pathogen.	☐	☐
d)	If the same pathogen attacks you after you have a vaccine you won't get sick.	☐	☐

Q3 The **MMR vaccine** protects you from **measles**.

a) What else does the MMR vaccine protect you from? Circle **two** answers.

rheumatic fever | meningitis | rubella | whooping cough | mumps

b) If the pathogen that causes measles mutated, would the vaccine still protect you?

Write 'yes' or 'no'. ....

Q4 What is a **pandemic**? Tick the answer.

A type of virus. ☐

A special type of white blood cell. ☐

When a virus spreads around the world. ☐

A toxin made by bacteria. ☐

Vaccines and Drugs

Q1 Which of these sentences are **true**? Tick **two** answers.

Painkillers are a type of drug. ☐
Painkillers get rid of the symptoms of a disease. ☐
Painkillers kill the pathogen that causes the disease. ☐
All drugs kill pathogens that cause disease. ☐

Q2 a) What is an **antibiotic**? Circle the answer.

A chemical made by white blood cells. **A type of scab made by the skin.**

A drug that kills bacteria. **A toxin made by bacteria.**

b) Are these sentences **true** or **false**? Tick the right boxes.

	True	False
Antibiotics only get rid of symptoms.	☐	☐
Viruses are killed by antibiotics.	☐	☐
One type of antibiotic can kill all types of bacteria.	☐	☐
Penicillin is a type of antibiotic.	☐	☐

Q3 Vaccines have **advantages** and **disadvantages**. Put the sentences about vaccines in the table below. One has been done for you.

You can have a bad reaction to a vaccine. **Vaccines don't always work.**
~~**Vaccinating lots of people helps stop epidemics.**~~
Vaccines stop you getting ill. **Vaccines have helped to get rid of some diseases in the UK.**

ADVANTAGES OF VACCINES	DISADVANTAGES OF VACCINES
1. Vaccinating lots of people helps stop epidemics.	1. ....
2.	2. ....
3.	

Antibiotic Resistance

Q1 Few people now die from diseases caused by bacteria. Why is this? Circle the answer.

because we have antibiotics	because bacteria mutate	because we have white blood cells	because bacteria are dying out

Q2 a) Circle the right words to complete the sentences.

Over time bacteria can **mutate** / **develop reflexes**.

Some changes can make the bacteria **septic** / **resistant** to antibiotics.

This means the antibiotics **will** / **won't** kill them.

b) Give an example of an antibiotic-resistant bacteria.

....

Q3 Complete the sentences. Use two of the words below.

reproduce **epidemic** **mutate**

Bacteria could .... to make a new type that no-one is immune to.

This bacteria could spread quickly between people. It could even cause an ....

Q4 What is an **epidemic**? Tick the right box.

- A big outbreak of a disease. ☐
- Where a pathogen spreads around the world. ☐
- A type of pathogen. ☐
- A type of antibiotic. ☐

Q5 How can we make it harder for bacteria to become **resistant** to **antibiotics**?

....

....

Testing Antibiotics

Q1 You can grow bacteria in a Petri dish. Draw lines to match the **start** of each sentence with its **ending**. One has been done for you.

Start	Ending
You should tape a lid onto the Petri dish...	... by passing it through a flame.
In industry bacteria are grown at high temperatures...	... so they grow really fast.
In a school the bacteria should be grown at 25 °C...	... to stop harmful bacteria growing.
You should sterilise the wire loop...	... to stop any bacteria in the air getting in.

Q2 The diagram shows **bacteria** growing in a **Petri dish**. Two paper discs with different antibiotics have been added.

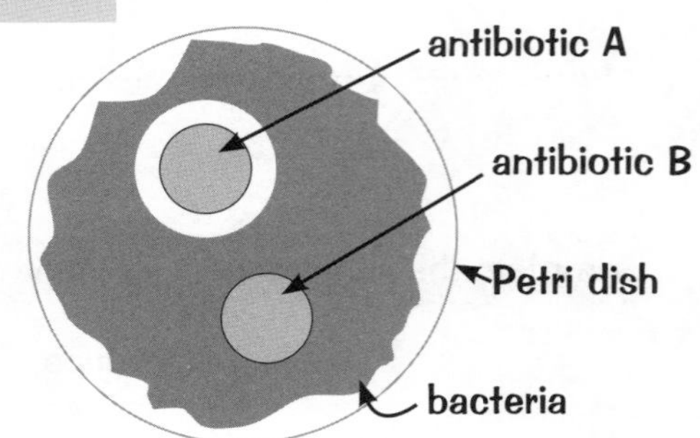

a) Which antibiotic has a clear patch around it? Circle the answer.

antibiotic A   antibiotic B

b) Which antibiotic are the bacteria resistant to? Circle the answer.

antibiotic A   antibiotic B

Q3 A man called **Semmelweis** made **doctors change** how they worked. The graph shows the percentage of women dying after giving birth before and after his change.

percentage of women dying after giving birth
12
10
8
6
4
2
before after

a) What percentage of women died **before** the change?

....

b) What did Semmelweis change? Circle the answer.

He told doctors to wash their hands before seeing patients.   He told patients to wash their hands before seeing doctors.

c) Why did less women die after Semmelweis's change? Tick the right box.

Because Semmelweis was a lucky mascot. ☐

Because there were no bacteria in the hospital anymore. ☐

Because the babies weren't passing bacteria to the women. ☐

Because the doctors weren't passing bacteria on their hands to the women. ☐

The Nervous System

Q1 What are **receptors**? Tick the right box.

- A sense organ. ☐
- A type of neurone. ☐
- Groups of cells that detect a stimulus. ☐
- Organs that decide what to do about a stimulus. ☐

Q2 Use the words below to complete the table.

skin **smell** **sound** **balance** **tongue**

Sense organ	Has receptors for
eyes	light
ears	1. .... 2. ....
nose	....
....	taste
....	hot and cold, touch, pressure, pain

Q3 Some parts of the body make up the **CNS**.

a) What do the letters 'CNS' stand for?

- ☐ central nervous system
- ☐ cardiac neurone system
- ☐ cellular nerve system

b) Name the **two** parts of the CNS.

1. ....

2. ....

The Nervous System

Q4 a) Draw lines to match the type of **neurone** with what they do.

Sensory neurones...	... carry information from the brain to effectors.
Motor neurones...	... carry information from receptors to the brain.

b) Name two types of **effectors**.

1. ....

2. ....

Q5 The diagram below shows how the **CNS** decides what to do. Label the diagram using the words in the box.

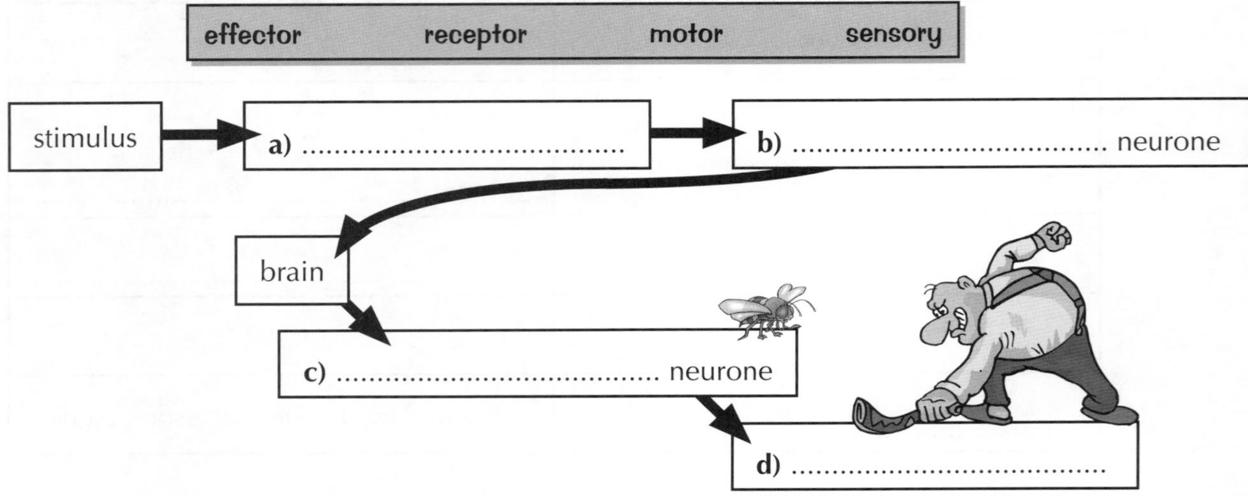

Q6 In the sentences below, what is the **sense organ** and what **stimulus** is it detecting? Write your answers in the table. One has been done for you.

	What is the sense organ?	What stimulus is it detecting?
Terry puts some lemon on his tongue. It tastes sour.	tongue	taste
Sarah wrinkles her nose. Something in the bin smells bad.		
Alex's ears are filled with the sound of the crowd cheering his goal.		
Lindsey cuts the skin on her hand. She cries.		

Reflexes and Synapses

Q1 **Circle** the right words to complete the sentences.

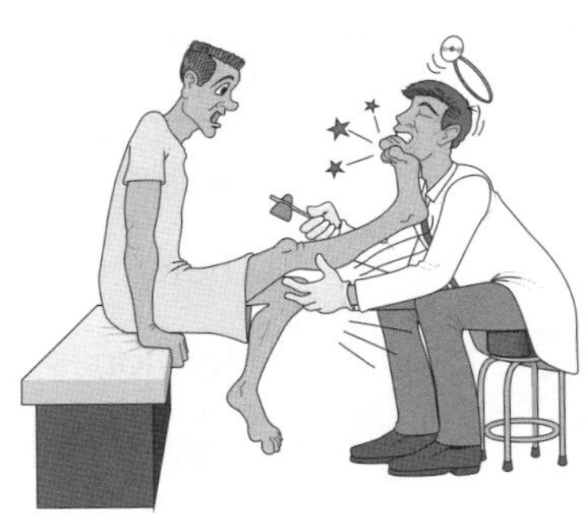

a) Reflexes are really **fast** / **slow**.

b) Reflexes stop you from **hurting** / **protecting** yourself.

c) Reflexes happen **with** / **without** you thinking about them.

d) A synapse is a tiny gap where two **receptors** / **neurones** join together.

e) **Chemicals** / **Impulses** take messages across synapses.

Q2 The diagram shows the path of a **reflex**.

a) Draw lines to match the letters from the diagram to their names. One has been done for you.

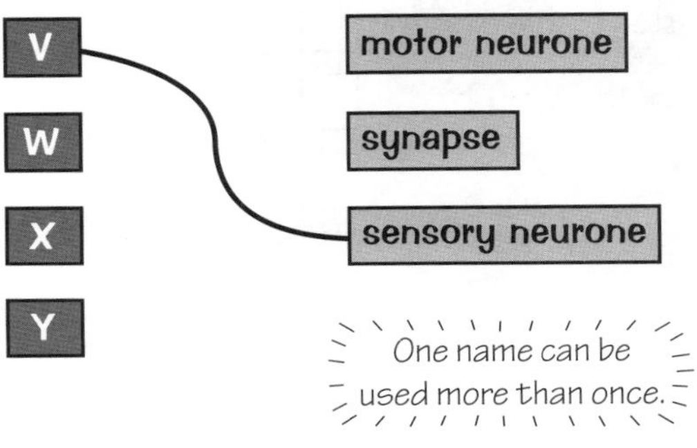

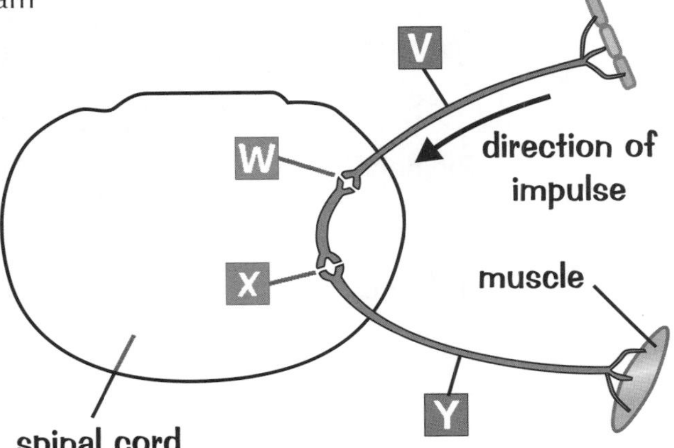

b) Circle the right words to complete the sentences below.

In this reflex the muscle acts as the **effector** / **receptor**.

The muscle responds by **contracting** / **releasing hormones**.

Q3 Write numbers in the boxes to show what happens at a **synapse**. The first one has been done for you.

The chemicals set off a new impulse in the next neurone.	
An impulse travels along a neurone.	1
Chemicals take the impulse across the synapse.	
The impulse reaches the end of the neurone.	

Hormones and the Menstrual Cycle

Q1 Circle the right words to complete the sentences.

Hormones are **impulses** / **chemicals**.

They're made in **glands** / **bone marrow**.

Hormones are carried **in the blood** / **along neurones** to other parts of the body.

They only affect certain cells, called **blood** / **target** cells.

Q2 What is the **menstrual cycle**? Tick **two** answers.

- The order that different hormones travel along nerves. ☐
- The release of an egg from a woman's ovaries every month. ☐
- The build-up and breakdown of the lining of the womb. ☐
- The build-up of hormones in the womb. ☐
- The order that a hormone affects target cells. ☐

Q3 What hormones are made by the body parts below?
Write down your answers using words from the box.

insulin	FSH	auxins	oestrogen

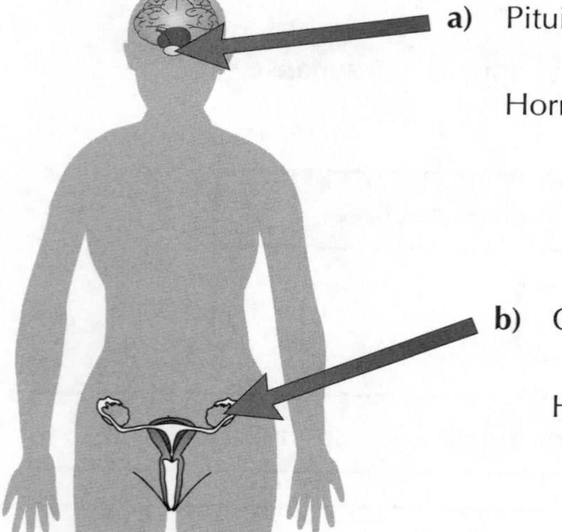

a) Pituitary gland

Hormone ....

b) Ovaries

Hormone ....

Hormones and the Menstrual Cycle

Q4 a) What does FSH stand for? Circle the answer.

Fertility-Stimulating Hormone **Follicle-Stimulating Hormone** **Fertility-Stunting Hormone**

b) What does LH stand for? Circle the answer.

Levelling Hormone **Lightening Hormone** **Luteinising Hormone**

Q5 Where are the hormones used in the menstrual cycle made? Complete the table.

HORMONE	WHERE IT IS MADE
FSH	
oestrogen	

Q6 a) Draw lines to match each hormone with its function.

FSH	stops FSH being released
LH	makes an egg mature in an ovary
Oestrogen	makes an ovary release its egg

b) Which hormone makes the ovaries release oestrogen?

....

Q7 Are these sentences **true** or **false**? Tick the right boxes.

		True	False
a)	A woman's ovaries release an egg every month.	☐	☐
b)	When the lining of the womb breaks down, a woman has her period.	☐	☐
c)	FSH and oestrogen don't affect each other.	☐	☐
d)	Nerve impulses control the menstrual cycle.	☐	☐
e)	All the hormones in the menstrual cycle do the same job.	☐	☐

The Pill

Q1 What is the **oral contraceptive pill**? Tick the answer.

A pill women take to help them get pregnant. ☐
A pill women take to stop them getting pregnant. ☐
A pill men take to stop them getting women pregnant. ☐

Q2 a) How does the pill work? Fill in the gaps using the words below.

The pill contains the hormone ....

FSH **oestrogen** **LH**

This stops .... being released.

FSH **oestrogen** **LH**

This means that .... so the woman can't get pregnant.

the ovaries shrink **no eggs mature** **embryos can't grow**

b) Name **one** other hormone that the pill contains.

....

Q3 Circle the right words to complete the sentences below.

The pill used to have **a lot of / not much** oestrogen in it. But people worried that this caused **multiple-births / side effects**. The pill now has **more / less** oestrogen in it. There's also a tablet called the **progesterone-only / FSH-only** pill. It only has **one / two** hormones in it. It causes fewer **multiple-births / side effects**.

Q4 Are these sentences **true** or **false**? Tick the right boxes.

		True	False
a)	There is no chance of getting pregnant if you take the pill.	☐	☐
b)	The pill can cause side effects, like headaches.	☐	☐
c)	The progesterone-only tablet has fewer side effects than the pill.	☐	☐

Getting Pregnant

Q1 Women can take **hormones** to help them get **pregnant**.

a) Which hormones can help a women get pregnant? Circle **two** answers.

progesterone LH FSH oestrogen

b) How do the hormones you circled in part **a)** help a woman get pregnant? Tick the answer.

☐ They make an egg mature and be released.

☐ They help an egg be fertilised by sperm.

☐ They help an embryo grow.

Q2 Put numbers in the boxes to show how **IVF** works.
The first one has been done for you.

[1] An egg is collected from the woman's ovary.

☐ The embryo is put inside the woman's womb.

☐ The embryo grows.

☐ The egg is joined with a man's sperm in a lab. This makes a fertilised egg.

☐ The fertilised egg becomes an embryo.

Q3 Are these sentences **true** or **false**? Tick the right boxes.

	True	False
a) IVF stands for invasive fertilisation.	☐	☐
b) The hormones in IVF can make some women sick.	☐	☐
c) IVF doesn't cause women to have twins or triplets.	☐	☐
d) IVF can help couples who can't have children to have a child.	☐	☐

Q4 Give **two** disadvantages of taking hormones to help get pregnant.

DISADVANTAGES

1. ....

2. ....

Plant Hormones

Q1 Are these sentences **true** or **false**? Tick the right boxes.

		True	False
a)	Plant shoots grow away from light.	☐	☐
b)	Plant roots grow upwards.	☐	☐
c)	Plant roots grow in the same direction as gravity.	☐	☐
d)	Plants grow in response to moisture.	☐	☐

Q2 Some plants are growing in a shed. It's lit by **electric lights**. Circle the letters above the **two** lights that have **broken**.

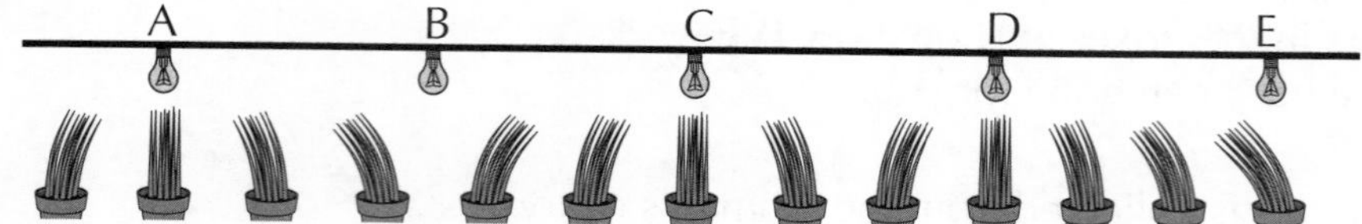

Q3 Draw lines to complete the sentences.

Phototropism means...

Gravitropism means...

... growing in response to gravity.

... growing in response to light.

Q4 Circle the right words to complete the sentences below.

When light shines on a **shoot**, auxin moves to the side in the **light / shade**. Auxin makes the cells there **grow faster / stop growing**. This means the shoot bends **upwards / downwards**.

In **roots**, gravity makes auxin move to the **upper / lower** side. Auxin makes the cells there **grow / stop growing**. This means the root bends **upwards / downwards**.

Plant Hormones

Q5 Circle the right words to complete the sentences.

Roots grow in moist soil. The auxin moves towards the **wet** / **dry** side of the roots. The auxin makes the cells there **grow faster** / **stop growing**. This means the root bends **towards** / **away from** the moisture.

Q6 Tick the sentence that is **false**.

Gravity makes shoots bend downwards. ☐

Weedkillers contain plant hormones. ☐

Plant hormones are used in rooting powder. ☐

Rooting powder helps plant cuttings to grow roots. ☐

Q7 Two seedlings were planted. **Nothing** was done to **seedling A**. A **plastic strip** was put into **seedling B**. They were left for five hours. The results are shown in the table.

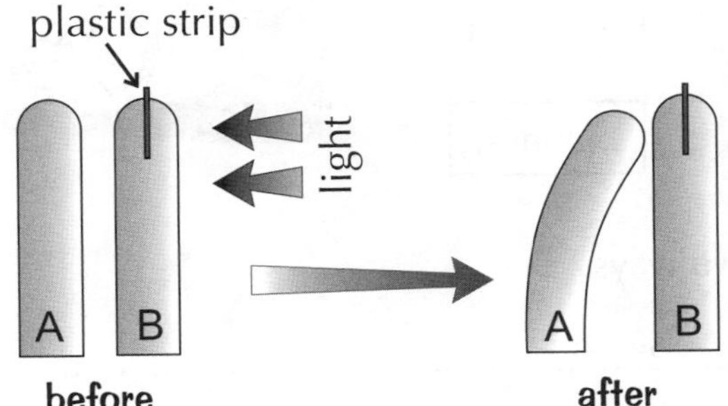

Seedling	What was done to the seedling	What happened after 5 hours
A	left alone	it bent towards the light
B	plastic strip through centre of tip	no change

a) What happened to seedling B after 5 hours? Circle your answer.

It bent away from the light. There was no change. It bent towards the light.

b) What is the reason for the results for seedling B? Tick the answer.

The plastic stopped the seedling making auxin. ☐

The plastic stopped auxin moving to the side in the shade. ☐

The plastic helped auxin move to the side in the light. ☐

The plastic made the seedling make too much auxin. ☐

Controlling Internal Conditions

Q1 Why does your body need to keep **conditions** inside it **steady**? Circle the answer.

so your cells can work properly | so your body can fight infections | so your cells don't become clogged with cholesterol

Q2 a) How does the body **get ions** (salt)?

....

b) How does the body **get rid** of too many ions? Tick **two** answers.

- ☐ The liver gets rid of ions.
- ☐ Ions are removed in urine.
- ☐ Ions are lost in sweat.
- ☐ Ions are lost in saliva.

Q3 a) Draw lines to complete the sentences.

Water is lost in sweat from the...	... kidneys.
Water is lost in breath from the...	... skin.
Water is lost in urine from the...	... lungs.

b) How does the body gain water? Write down **two** ways.

1. .... 2. ....

Q4 Why does your body need to keep its **temperature** steady? Circle the answer.

so enzymes can work | so hormones can work | so blood doesn't clot

Q5 Why does your body need to keep its level of **sugar** steady?

....

Drugs

Q1 a) What do **drugs** do? Underline the answer.

They carry messages around your body. They change the chemical reactions in your body.

b) What does addicted mean? Tick **two** answers.

- ☐ You want a drug really badly.
- ☐ You need to get a prescription for the drug.
- ☐ You can get withdrawal symptoms if the drug isn't taken.

c) Which of the following are very addictive drugs? Circle **two** answers.

heroin cocaine auxin toast progesterone

Q2 Are these sentences **true** or **false**? Tick the right boxes.

		True	False
a)	Some drugs are medicines.	☐	☐
b)	Statins are a performance enhancing drug.	☐	☐
c)	Statins increase the risk of heart and circulatory diseases.	☐	☐
d)	You need a prescription from your doctor for statins.	☐	☐

Q3 Some athletes use **performance-enhancing drugs**.

a) Draw lines to match the drug to its effect on the body.

Steroids...	... make your muscles bigger.
Stimulants...	... make your heart rate faster.

b) Some people won't use performance-enhancing drugs. Circle the reason why.

They aren't addictive enough. They can have bad health effects. They make people sweat more.

Q4 Are these reasons **for** or **against** taking performance-enhancing drugs? Tick the right boxes.

		For	Against
a)	It's not fair if people are better at sports just because of drugs.	☐	☐
b)	Sport isn't fair. For example, different athletes may have different coaches.	☐	☐
c)	Athletes can make their own decisions about their health.	☐	☐
d)	Athletes may not know about the bad health effects.	☐	☐

Testing Medicines

Q1 Write numbers 1-3 in the boxes to show the order that **drugs** are **tested** in.

☐ Drug is tested on healthy volunteers.

☐ Ill volunteers are used to test the drug.

☐ Drug is tested on human cells and tissues in a laboratory.

DRUG TEST
9 - 11 am

Q2 Draw lines to complete the sentences. One has been done for you.

Drugs are tested on healthy volunteers to...

Drugs are tested on ill volunteers to...

Drugs are tested on human cells and tissues in a laboratory to...

... check the drug is effective.

... check the drug is safe.

... find the dose that works best.

Q3 **Placebos** are used in some drug trials.

a) What is a placebo? Circle the answer.

A drug that we know works. | A painkiller. | A type of energy drink. | A fake medicine that doesn't do anything.

b) Why are people given placebos in a drug trial? Tick the answer.

Placebos help check that it's really the drug making people better. ☐

Placebos help check that any side effects aren't because of the drug. ☐

c) What is a double blind trial? Tick the answer.

☐ It's where the people who make the drugs and placebos don't know which is which.

☐ It's where patients have to wear a blindfold when taking their medicine.

☐ It's where the doctors and patients don't know which patients have taken the drug and which have taken the placebo.

Thalidomide

Q1 What was **thalidomide** tested to be used for? Tick the answer.

- To treat diabetes. ☐
- As a sleeping pill. ☐
- To treat heart disease. ☐
- As a painkiller. ☐
- As a vaccine for rubella. ☐

Q2 Betty was **pregnant**. She was given **thalidomide**.

a) Why was Betty given thalidomide? Circle the answer.

To give her lots of iron.

To treat her morning sickness.

To help her heart.

b) What did the thalidomide do to Betty's baby? Circle the answer.

It helped the baby grow.

It gave the baby lots of iron.

It harmed the baby.

Q3 a) Was thalidomide **tested** to be used on pregnant women? Circle the answer.

YES **NO**

b) What did using thalidomide to treat pregnant women lead to? Tick **two** answers.

- Thalidomide was banned. ☐
- Drugs began to be tested on pregnant women. ☐
- Placebos were used to treat morning sickness. ☐
- Drug testing became more strict. ☐

c) What illness is thalidomide now used to treat? Circle the answer.

diabetes **chicken pox** **leprosy** **heart disease**

Recreational Drugs

Q1 a) Which **health problems** can drinking **alcohol** lead to? Circle **two** answers.

mumps   liver damage   lung disease   brain damage

b) Which health problems can be caused by **smoking**? Circle **two** answers.

tuberculosis   lung disease   lung cancer   unconsciousness

Q2 a) Which of these are recreational drugs? Tick **three** answers.

☐ cannabis   ☐ statins   ☐ antibiotics   ☐ heroin   ☐ ecstasy

b) Why might people take recreational drugs? Write down **one** reason.

....

c) Which health problem can illegal drugs cause? Underline **one** answer.

diabetes   deficiency diseases   heart and circulatory problems

polio   mumps

Q3 A study looked at the **link** between the use of **cannabis** and the use of **hard drugs**. Some results are shown in the graph.

What does the study show? Tick the answer.

Cannabis is less dangerous than hard drugs. ☐

More people use cannabis than hard drugs. ☐

Cannabis use leads to hard drug use. ☐

No. of drug users

Cannabis   Hard drug

Q4 Why do **alcohol** and **smoking** have a **bigger effect** than illegal drugs in the UK? Tick the answer.

Because alcohol and smoking are more dangerous than illegal drugs. ☐

Because fewer people take legal drugs than illegal drugs. ☐

Because more people take legal drugs than illegal drugs. ☐

Because smoking makes people want to try hard drugs. ☐

Smoking and alcohol are both legal.

Mixed Questions — Biology 1a

Q1 The diagram shows a woman's **menstrual cycle**.

a) How long does the woman's **menstrual cycle** last?

.... days.

b) Which hormones control the menstrual cycle?
Circle **three** answers.

FSH **oestrogen** **auxin** **LH** **insulin**

0
menstrual period
4
8
12
16
20
24
Day 14

c) The oral contraceptive pill contains oestrogen. How can oestrogen stop a woman becoming pregnant? Tick the answer.

- [ ] Oestrogen stops FSH being released. This means no eggs will mature.
- [ ] Oestrogen stops sperm from fertilising eggs.
- [ ] Oestrogen stops embryos from growing.

Q2 Are these sentences **true** or **false**? Tick the right boxes.

	True	False
a) Heroin is a very addictive drug.	☐	☐
b) Alcohol is legal.	☐	☐
c) Alcohol isn't harmful.	☐	☐
d) Addictive drugs don't give you withdrawal symptoms.	☐	☐

Q3 a) Circle the right words to complete the sentences.

Cigarettes / **Vitamins** are needed to keep you healthy.

Overeating / **Undereating** can cause obesity.

People with lots of muscle usually have a **fast** / **slow** metabolic rate.

Carbohydrates give you **energy** / **materials to build new cells**.

Supavit

The body needs to keep the amount of water inside it steady.

b) How is water **lost** from the body? Write down **three** ways.

1. ....

2. ....

3. ....

Mixed Questions — Biology 1a

Q4 Gavin is running a race.

a) The crowds cheer Gavin on. Which of his **sense organs** hears the cheers? Circle the answer.

ears eyes nose tongue skin

Information travels around Gavin's body along neurones.

b) What is the difference between **sensory** and **motor neurones**? Tick the answer.

☐ Sensory neurones are only found in the CNS. Motor neurones are found in the whole body.

☐ There is no difference.

☐ Sensory neurones carry messages from receptors to the brain. Motor neurones carry messages from the brain to effectors.

c) What is the gap between neurones called?

....

d) Gavin has taken **steroids**. Why might he have done this? Circle the answer.

to increase his heart rate to give him energy to make him better at sports

Q5 Bacteria were grown in a Petri dish. Discs of filter paper soaked in three different antibiotics were put in the Petri dish. The diagram shows the results.

a) What has happened in the clear zone around discs 1 and 3? Tick the answer.

☐ The filter paper has mutated the bacteria.

☐ The bacteria have eaten the antibiotics.

☐ Antibiotics have killed the bacteria.

discs 1-3 (soaked in different antibiotics)
1
2
3
Petri dish
bacteria
clear zone

b) Which antibiotic worked best? Circle the answer.

Antibiotic 1 Antibiotic 2 Antibiotic 3

c) Why won't this antibiotic work against viruses?

....

Adaptations

Q1 What are **adaptations**? Tick the answer.

- A type of desert animal. ☐
- Features that help plants and animals to survive. ☐
- A group of bacteria that live in tough environments. ☐

Q2 Complete these sentences. Use the words below.

a) Lots of animals find it hard to survive in the desert. This is because it's very ....

windy **hot** **wet**

b) Lots of animals find it hard to survive in the arctic. This is because it's very ....

hot **cold**

Q3 The arctic fox is adapted to living in the **arctic**.

a) What features help it keep in heat? Circle **two** answers.

a thick coat **big eyes** **a thin tail** **long claws** **lots of body fat**

b) The fox has white fur. How does this feature help it avoid predators? Tick the answer.

- ☐ It makes the fox more dangerous.
- ☐ It makes the fox hard to see.
- ☐ It warns predators that the fox could be poisonous.

Q4 The kangaroo rat lives in the **desert**.

a) Which **two** features on the diagram help the kangaroo rat to survive?

1. ....

2. ....

b) The kangaroo rat has camouflage. What is camouflage? Circle the answer.

Camouflage makes an animal hard to see. **Camouflage is a type of poison sting.**

Camouflage is a type of fur that helps animals lose less water.

Adaptations

Q5 Complete these sentences. Use the words below.

a) Lots of plants can't survive in the desert. This is because it's very ....

sandy wet dry

b) Some microorganisms can survive in tough places. For example, very .... lakes.

salty wet dry

Q6 Some plants and animals are adapted to scare away predators.

a) What are **predators**? Underline the answer.

They're animals that eat other plants and animals. | They're plants that get eaten by animals. | They're animals that steal other animals' homes.

b) What **adaptations** do plants and animals have for scaring away predators? Circle **three** answers.

thorns camouflage poisons in stings warning colours thick fur a round shape

Q7 Circle the right words to complete the sentences.

Some microorganisms are adapted to live in tough environments. They're called **extremophiles / toughophiles**. For example, they live in places like **hedges / the bottom of the sea**. They're also found **on grass / in volcanoes**.

Q8 a) Where are cactus plants usually found? Underline the answer.

in arctic regions in the desert by lakes on active volcanoes

b) Draw lines to complete the sentences.

The cactus plant has spines because...

The cactus plant has long roots...

The cactus plant has a thick stem...

... to get as much water as possible.

... to store water for when there's not much around.

... they lose less water than leaves.

Competition and Environmental Change

Q1 a) Draw lines to match plants and animals with the things they need.

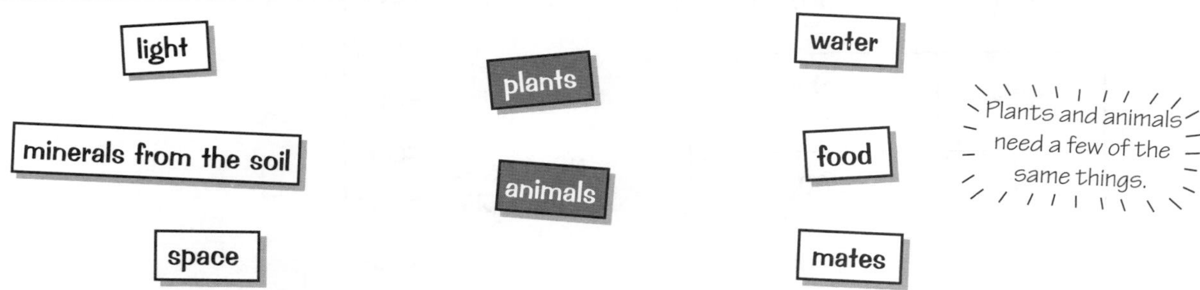

b) Circle the right word to complete the sentence below.

If lots of organisms need the same thing, they will **compete for / share** it.

c) What do organisms get from other living things? Circle **two** answers.

oxygen   mates   water   food   space

Q2 **Algae** are tiny organisms that are eaten by **fish**. The graph shows how the number of algae in a pond changed in a year.

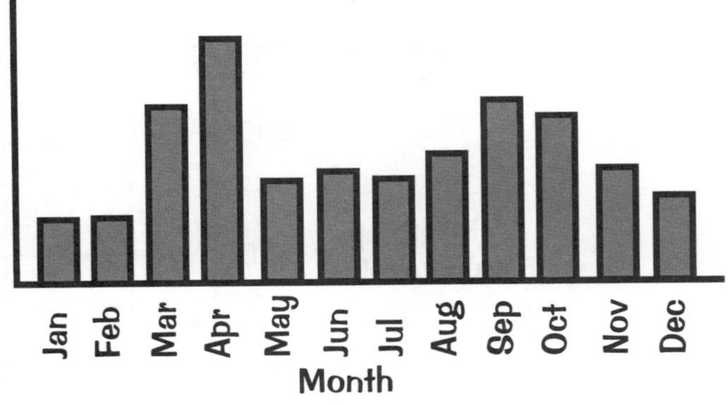

a) What month had the most algae? Circle the answer.

January   July

April   October

b) Why might there have been more algae in this month? Tick **two** boxes.

Factor	
The temperature of the water changed.	
There were more fish eating the algae.	
There were more algae diseases.	
There were less fish eating the algae.	

Competition and Environmental Change

Q3 The table shows how the number of barn owls has changed over 20 years.

Year	Number of barn owls
1970	7000
1980	4500
1990	1700

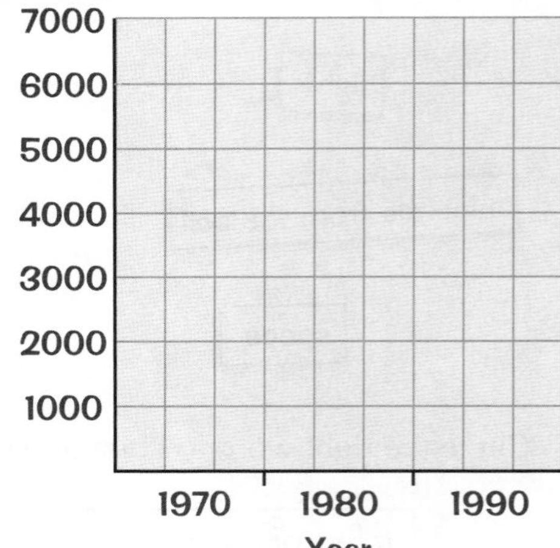

a) Draw a **bar chart** to show how the number of barn owls has changed. Use the data in the table.

b) Circle the right word to complete the sentence.

The bar chart shows the number of barn owls **falling** / **rising** between 1970 and 1990.

c) What **living thing** could have caused the change in the number of barn owls? Circle the answer.

warmer temperature **fewer predators** **less food for them to eat** **more rain**

Q4 The graph shows how high up a mountain a type of snail was found over the last 100 years.

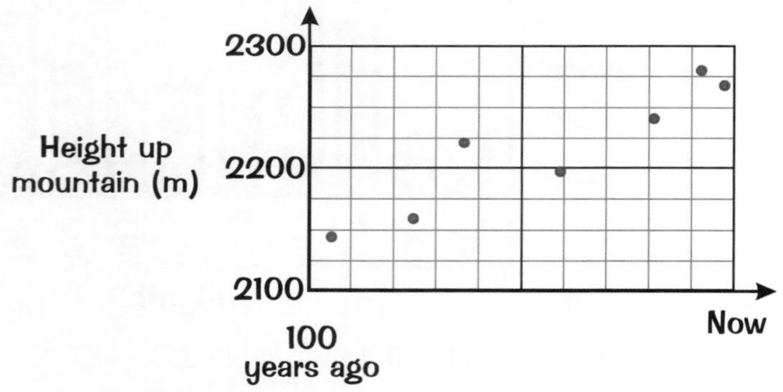

a) What does the graph show? Tick the right box.

- [ ] Snails now live higher up the mountain than they did 100 years ago.
- [ ] The snails live at the same height up the mountain now as they did 100 years ago.
- [ ] Snails now live lower down the mountain than they did 100 years ago.

b) What could have caused the change in where the snails live? Circle the answer.

There was a change in the environment. **The snails became more curious.** **There were more predators higher up the mountain.**

Measuring Environmental Change

Q1 Are these sentences **true** or **false**? Tick the right boxes.

		True	False
a)	Rain gauges measure how much rain falls.	☐	☐
b)	Living indicators are organisms that are affected by changes in their environment.	☐	☐
c)	Oxygen meters measure how much carbon there is in water.	☐	☐

Q2 The diagram shows a sewage outlet by a river. The number of mayfly larvae were measured at three distances from it. The results are shown in the table.

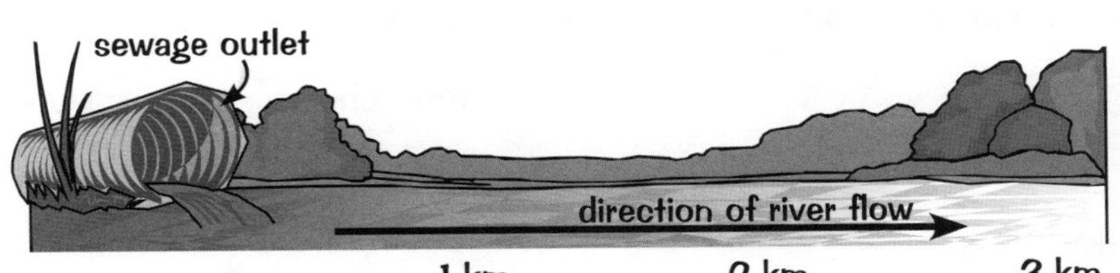

Distance (km) from sewage outlet	No. of mayfly larvae
1	3
2	11
3	23

a) What do the results show? Tick the answer.

☐ Mayfly larvae prefer clean water. ☐ Mayfly larvae prefer water containing sewage.

b) Circle the right word to explain the answer to part **a)**.

Mayfly larvae need lots of oxygen to live.
Clean water / polluted water has lots of oxygen in it.

Q3 The graph shows the amount of sulfur dioxide given out between 1970 and 2003.

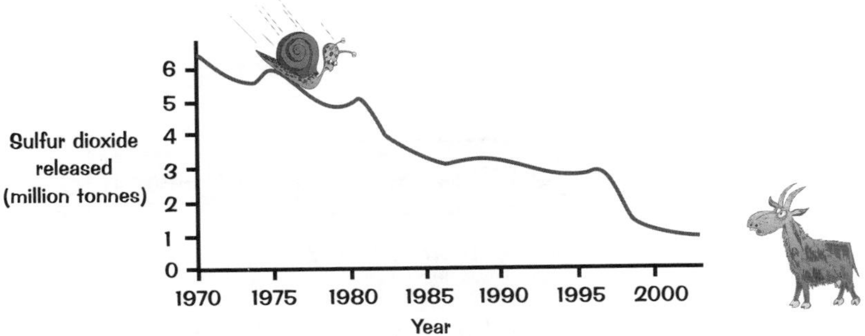

a) In what year was the largest amount of sulfur dioxide released? Circle the answer.

1970 **1975** **1980** **1985**

b) How much sulfur dioxide was released in 2003? Circle the answer.

1 million tonnes **2 million tonnes** **4 million tonnes**

c) Circle the right word to complete the sentence.

Lichen / Sludgeworms are good living indicators for sulfur dioxide.

Pyramids of Biomass

Q1 What is **biomass**? Circle the right answer.

the number of living things in a food chain — how much living things weigh — the number of living things left at the end of a food chain

Q2 Complete the sentences using the words below.

a) A food chain shows ....

what is eaten by what — how animals lose biomass

b) A pyramid of biomass shows the amount of biomass at each stage of a ....

food chain — carbon cycle

Q3 Look at the **pyramid of biomass**.

crab
winkle
algae

a) Circle the right word to complete the sentence.

The winkles are eating the **crabs / algae**.

b) Which organism has the biggest biomass? Circle the answer.

algae — winkle — crab

c) What happens to the biomass as you go up the food chain? Circle the answer.

The amount of biomass goes down. — The amount of biomass goes up. — The amount of biomass doesn't change.

Q4 Look at the **food chain**.

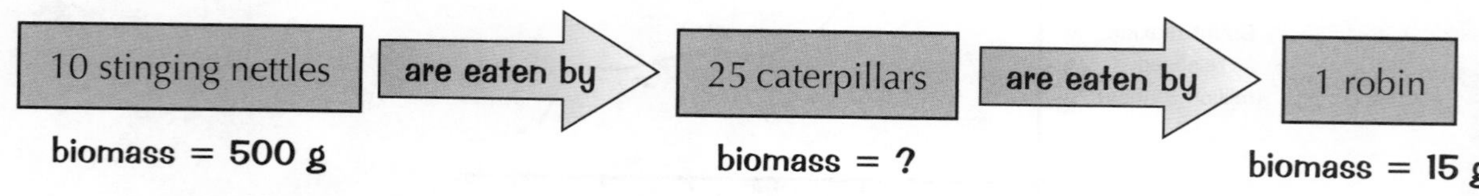

a) One caterpillar weighs 2 g. What is the total biomass of caterpillars in the food chain?

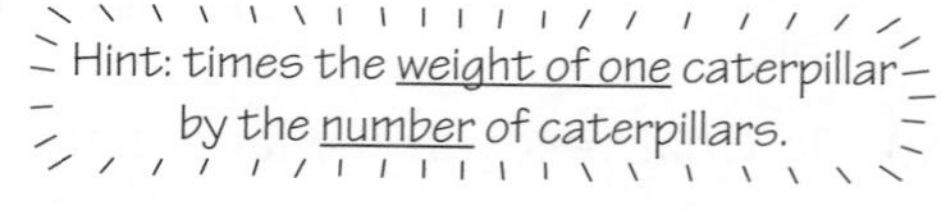

....

b) Circle the picture which shows a pyramid of biomass for the food chain above.

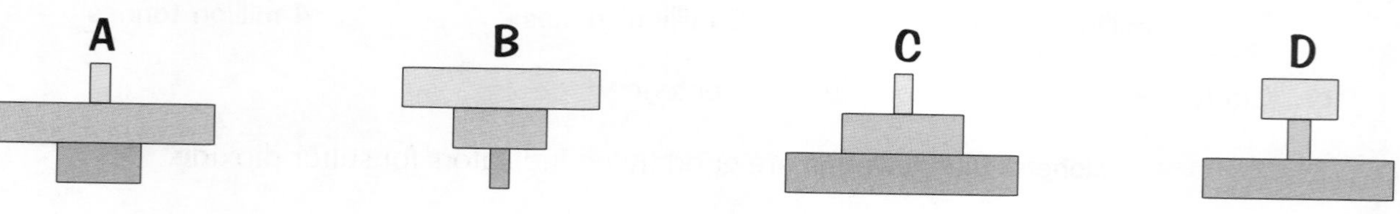

Energy Transfer and Decay

Q1 Are these sentences **true** or **false**? Tick the right boxes.

		True	False
a)	All energy comes from the Sun.	☐	☐
b)	Plants use the Sun's energy to make food.	☐	☐
c)	The energy from photosynthesis can't be stored in plant cells.	☐	☐
d)	Energy is passed along food chains by eating.	☐	☐
e)	Animals make energy through photosynthesis.	☐	☐

Q2 a) What happens to the amount of **energy** at each stage of a food chain? Circle the answer.

Each stage has less energy than the one before.

Each stage has more energy than the one before.

b) How is energy lost from a food chain? Circle **two** answers.

as heat from respiration | **during photosynthesis** | **as waste products** | **leakage from plant cells** | **by eating**

Q3 Compost bins are used to break down kitchen waste.

a) What do microorganisms in compost bins need to break down waste? Circle **three** answers.

sludge | **warmth** | **growth hormones** | **oxygen** | **moisture**

b) Circle the right words to complete the sentences below.

> **Compost** / **Energy** forms at the bottom of compost bins.
> It's made up of **chemicals** / **hormones** released from decay.
> It can be put on your garden for plants to use for **growing** / **decaying**.

Q4 Circle the right words to complete the sentences.

> Living organisms are made up of **materials** / **adaptations** they take from the world around them. Waste and dead organisms are **preserved** / **broken down** by microorganisms. This is called **competition** / **decay**. It puts **materials** / **adaptations** back into the environment.

The Carbon Cycle

Q1 Circle the right words to complete the sentences.

Plants take carbon dioxide out of the air by **photosynthesis** / **respiration**. They use the carbon from carbon dioxide to make things like **sulfur dioxide** / **carbohydrates**. Animals get carbon by **eating** / **respiring**. They use it to make things like fats and **lichen** / **proteins**. Carbon is released back into the air by plants and animals by **photosynthesis** / **respiration**.

Q2 Draw lines to complete the sentences.

Plants use carbon to make...	break down dead organisms and waste material.
Microorganisms...	carbon dioxide is taken out of the air.
When plants and animals respire...	by eating plants.
Animals get carbon...	carbohydrates, fats and proteins.
During photosynthesis...	carbon dioxide goes back into the air.

Q3 The diagram below shows the **carbon cycle**.

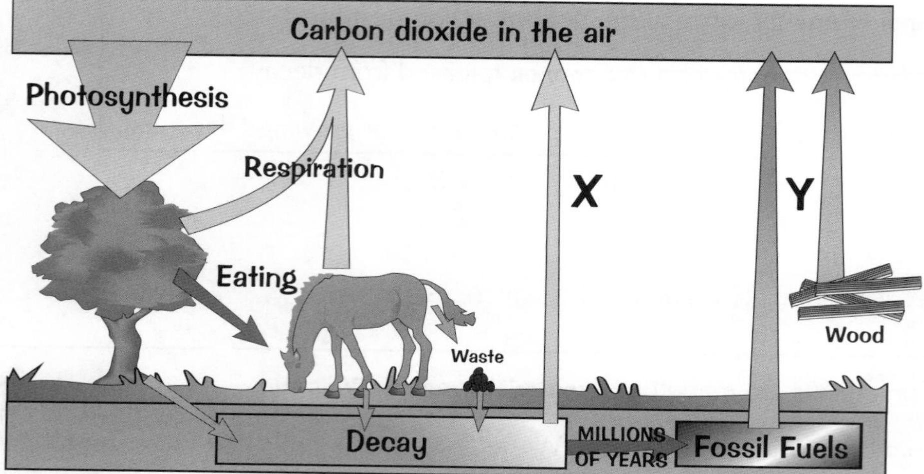

a) What is process **X**? ....

b) What is process **Y**? ....

Genes and Chromosomes

Q1 Use the words in the box to complete the sentences.

Most cells in your body have a **synapse** / **nucleus**.

This structure contains **muscles** / **chromosomes**.

Different characteristics are controlled by **fats** / **genes**.

Q2 Add the correct label to each diagram. Use the words from the box.

gene	chromosome	nucleus

a)

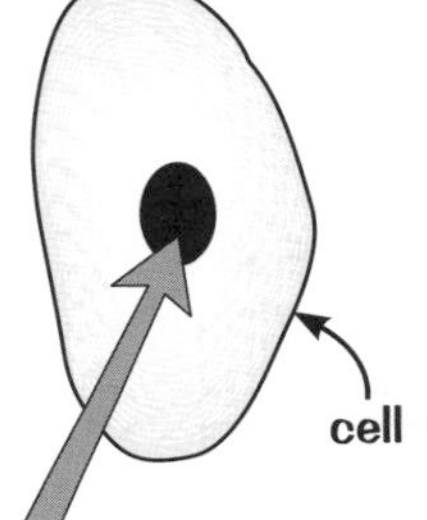

....

b)

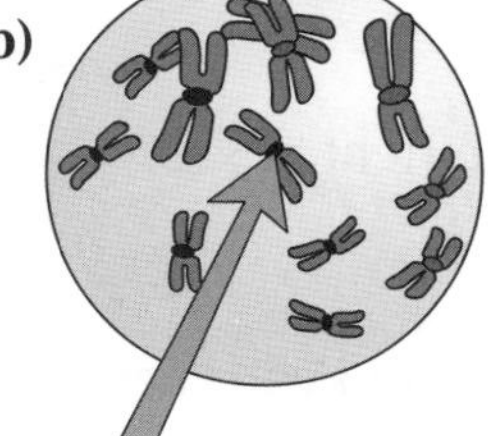

....

c)

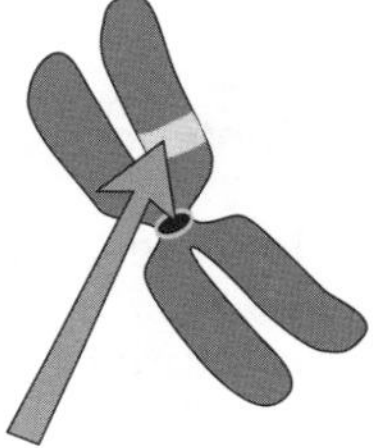

....

Q3 Which sentences are **true**? Tick **three** boxes.

- Chromosomes carry a nucleus. ☐
- Genes control what characteristics a plant or animal has. ☐
- The same genes control different characteristics. ☐
- You get your genes from your parents. ☐
- Plants and animals look like their parents because they share genes. ☐

Variation

Q1 a) Circle the right word to complete the sentence.

Plants and animals of the same kind have **exactly the same / different** characteristics.

b) Complete the sentence using one of the words below.

Differences in characteristics are called ....

cloning **variation** **reproduction**

c) Tick the sentence which is **true**.

- ☐ Variation is caused only by the environment.
- ☐ Variation is caused by genes, the environment or both.
- ☐ Variation is caused only by genes.

Q2 Are these sentences **true** or **false**? Tick the right boxes.

		True	False
a)	Everyone has the same genes.	☐	☐
b)	You get a mixture of genes from your mum and your dad.	☐	☐
c)	The height of a plant is controlled by its genes and the environment.	☐	☐
d)	Some characteristics are controlled only by the environment.	☐	☐

Q3 Helen and Stephanie are identical twins. They have the **same genes**.

a) Helen weighs more than Stephanie. Is this because of their genes, the environment or both? Circle the answer.

genes **environment** **both genes and environment**

b) Stephanie has a birthmark. Helen doesn't. Are birthmarks caused by genes? Circle the answer.

Yes. Birthmarks are caused by genes. Helen must have faulty genes.

No. Stephanie and Helen have the same genes.
If birthmarks were caused by genes they'd both have one.

Reproduction

Q1 Draw lines to complete the sentences.

Sexual reproduction is where...	... one cell splits into two.
Asexual reproduction is where...	... two gametes fuse to make a new cell.

Q2 Use the words in the box to label the diagram.

gametes	egg	new cell	sperm

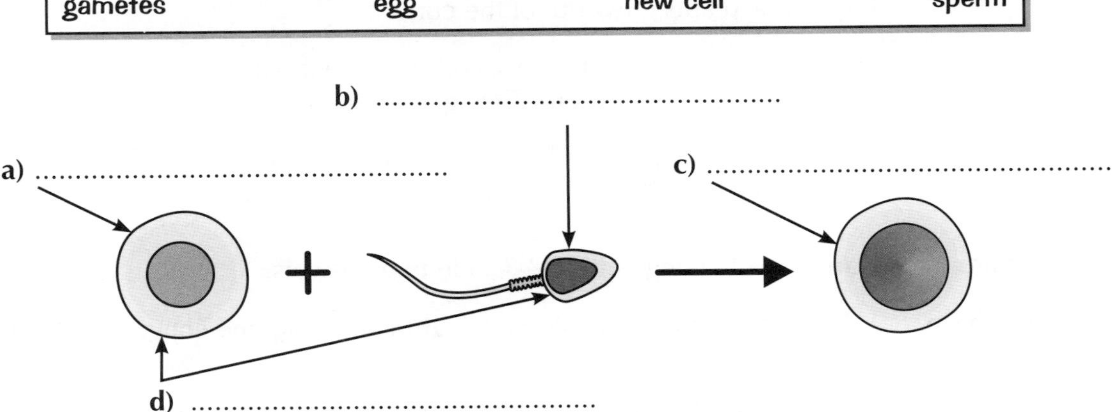

Q3 Circle the right words to complete the sentences.

a) Sexual reproduction involves **one gamete** / **two gametes**.

b) In sexual reproduction the sex cells are called **clones** / **gametes**.

c) Asexual reproduction makes offspring with **identical** / **different** genes to the parent.

d) **Asexual** / **Sexual** reproduction makes offspring that are different to the parent(s).

e) In **asexual** / **sexual** reproduction there is no mixing of genes.

Q4 Complete the sentences using the words below them.

a) Offspring that have the same genes as their parent are called ....

gametes **clones** **Dave**

b) In animals the male gamete is the ....

gene **egg** **sperm**

c) In sexual reproduction the gametes from each parent ....

fuse together **split apart** **swap genes**

Billy...?

Cloning

Q1 a) Complete the sentences. Use the words below.

You can make copies of plants. These are called ....

clones **embryos** **genes**

All the copies of a plant contain the same ....

genes **embryos** **herbicides**

b) Plant clones can be made by taking cuttings. What steps are involved in taking cuttings? Tick the answer.

☐ You make long cuts in the stem of a parent plant. New plants grow out of the cuts.

☐ You cut some small pieces off the parent plant. You pop them in soil. They grow into new plants.

☐ You cut the parent plant into pieces. You burn the pieces. New plants grow out of the ashes.

c) What are the **advantages** of taking cuttings? Circle **two** answers.

It's cheap. **Disease can't kill the plants.** **It makes only one copy.** **It's quick.**

d) Name **one** other way of making copies of a plant. ....

Q2 The diagram shows how **embryos** can be **cloned**.

Draw a line to match each description to the stage on the diagram. One has been done for you.

An embryo develops.	The embryos are put into other cows to grow.	The cells are split up.	The egg and sperm of a cow and bull are fused together.	Each cell grows into a new embryo.	The baby calves have the same genes as each other. They're clones.

A B C D E F

Cloning

Q3 The diagram shows how to **clone** an **adult** animal.

Where do the labels below belong on the diagram?
Write the correct letter next to each label.
The first one (A) has been done for you.

Take the nucleus out of an egg cell ......A......

Put the embryo into an adult female ....

Take the nucleus out of an adult body cell ....

Put the nucleus from the body cell into the empty egg cell ....

Q4 **Adult cell cloning** was used to make Bob.

Are these sentences **true** or **false**? Tick the right boxes.

		True	False
a)	The embryo has the same genes as Daisy.	☐	☐
b)	Gerald has the same genes as Bob.	☐	☐
c)	The egg cell needed an electric shock to make it into an embryo.	☐	☐
d)	The embryo contains Daisy and Gerald's genes.	☐	☐

Q5 What are the **advantages** and **disadvantages** of **cloning**? Put the sentences into the table below.

Studying clones might help us understand some diseases.

Cloned animals might not be as healthy as normal ones.

A new disease could kill a group of clones all at once.

You can make lots of copies of a perfect plant or animal.

ADVANTAGES OF CLONING:	DISADVANTAGES OF CLONING:
1.	1. ....
2.	2. ....

Genetic Engineering

Q1 Genetic engineering can be used to put **genes** from humans into bacteria.

Draw lines to match the labels to the diagrams. One has been done for you.

A gene on a human chromosome.

The human gene is put into the bacteria.

Gene is cut out of human DNA.

The bacteria's chromosome is cut open.

A

B

C

D

Q2 a) Circle the right words to complete the sentences.

New genes can be put into very **young** / **old** plants and animals.

The new gene gives them a **useless** / **useful** characteristic.

GM stands for **genetically malleable** / **genetically modified**.

GM crops have had their genes **changed** / **removed**.

b) Give **one** example of a useful characteristic that has been given to plants using genetic engineering.

....

Q3 Are these sentences **advantages** or **disadvantages** of GM crops? Tick the right boxes.

		Advantage	Disadvantage
a)	GM crops could affect the number of flowers and insects nearby.	☐	☐
b)	You can add vitamins to GM crops.	☐	☐
c)	GM crops have a higher yield than normal crops.	☐	☐
d)	Some people think GM crops aren't safe to eat.	☐	☐

Evolution

Q1 Circle the right words to complete the sentences.

The first organisms appeared three **billion** / **hundred** years ago.

The first organisms were very **complex** / **simple**.

Over time organisms have become more **complex** / **simple**.

Some / **All** living things today evolved from these first organisms.

Q2 a) What characteristics do **plants** have? Circle **one** answer.

Their genes are found in the cell wall.	They all move around.	Their cells don't have a nucleus.	They make their own food.

b) What characteristics do **animals** have? Circle **one** answer.

Their genes are found in the cell wall.	They all move around.	Their cells don't have a nucleus.	They make their own food.

Q3 Are these sentences **true** or **false**? Tick the right boxes.

		True	False
a)	Our genes don't control any of our characteristics.	☐	☐
b)	Organisms that look similar usually have similar genes.	☐	☐
c)	Genes are passed down through families.	☐	☐
d)	Organisms with similar genes aren't always related.	☐	☐

Q4 The diagram shows how four species are related.

Dolphins Mice Rays Sharks

Which pair of animals is the **most closely** related? Tick the answer.

☐ Mice and Rays ☐ Rays and Sharks ☐ Mice and Sharks

Natural Selection and Mutations

Q1 a) What is **natural selection**? Underline the answer.

It's how evolution happens.   It's how the planet was formed.

It's how exam marks are given.

b) Who came up with the idea of natural selection? Circle the answer.

Isaac Newton   Dorothy Garrod   Elizabeth Gaskell   Marie Curie   Lamarck   Charles Darwin

Q2 Complete the sentences to show how **natural selection** works. Use the words given below.

An example has been done for you.

Living things of the same type have slightly different ....genes.......... .

genes   blood cells

a) This means there's lots of .... between them.

variation   jealousy

b) Some living things have characteristics that make them more likely to ....

survive   mutate

c) The ones with these characteristics are more likely to ....

breed   vary

d) This means they're more likely to .... their genes.

pass on   adapt

e) These characteristics become more ....

common   useful

Q3 a) What is a **mutation**? Underline the answer.

a type of evolution   a type of reproduction   a change in a gene

b) Which of these sentences are **true**? Tick **two** answers.

- Mutations never make useful characteristics. ☐
- Some mutations can help plants or animals to survive. ☐
- Plants or animals that survive are less likely to pass on mutations. ☐
- A mutation becomes more common among plants and animals by natural selection. ☐

More About Evolution

Q1 Why **didn't people agree** with **Darwin** when he first came up with the idea of natural selection? Circle **three** letters.

A He couldn't explain how new features appeared or were passed on.

B Characteristics caused by the environment can be passed on.

C People thought he made up the evidence.

D His ideas went against the Church.

E There wasn't much evidence.

F People didn't trust men with beards.

Q2 Circle the right words to complete the sentences.

A French chap called **Bismarck** / **Lamarck** had a different idea about how evolution worked. He thought that if a characteristic was used a lot it would become **more** / **less** developed. For example, if an anteater used its tongue a lot to reach ants in anthills, its tongue would get **longer** / **shorter**. He thought this characteristic would be passed on to **the next generation** / **animals living nearby**.

Q3 a) Why do people now accept **Darwin's** theory? Underline the answer.

- The Church says life on Earth was made by God.
- There's lots of evidence for it now.
- It's been proven to be true by maths.
- We now trust people with beards.

b) Why do people think **Lamarck's** theory is wrong? Underline the answer.

- The Church says life on Earth was made by God.
- There's no evidence for it.
- It's been proven to be wrong by maths.
- We still don't trust people with beards.

Mixed Questions — Biology 1b

Q1 The graph shows how the **body temperatures** of a camel and a goat change throughout the day in a hot desert.

a) What happened to the body temperature of the camel during the day? Underline the answer.

body temperature
camel
goat
6 am
12 noon
6 pm
12 midnight

It fell and then rose. It stayed the same.

It rose and then fell.

b) What happened to the body temperature of the goat during the day? Underline the answer.

It fell and then rose. It rose and then fell. It stayed the same.

c) Which animal can control its body heat better?

Think about which animal can keep its body temperature low when it's hotter.

....

d) Camels have evolved to lose heat. What is the name of Darwin's theory of evolution? Circle the answer.

natural breeding natural selection selective breeding genetic engineering

Q2 Scientists put the human gene for **growth hormone** into bacteria.

a) Complete the sentences. Use the words below.

The gene was cut from the human ....

chromosome enzymes bacteria

This was done using ....

bacteria genes enzymes

Then a .... from the bacteria is cut open.

gene chromosome enzymes

The human gene is put into this.

Afterwards, the bacteria were grown on agar plates.

b) All of the bacteria that grew had the same genes.
What type of reproduction took place?

....

Atoms and Elements

Q1 **Fill in** the table below. Use the words on the right.

Part of the atom	Charge
Proton	
	Neutral
Electron	

Negative

Neutron

Positive

Q2 Label the **atom** using the words in the box.

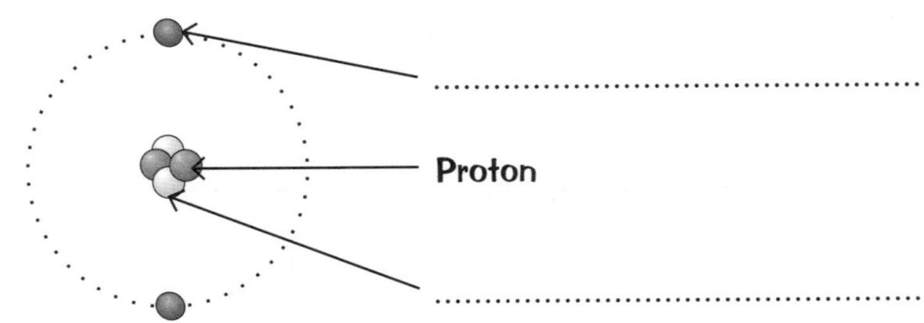

Q3 Look at these diagrams of substances. Circle the **two** that are **elements**.

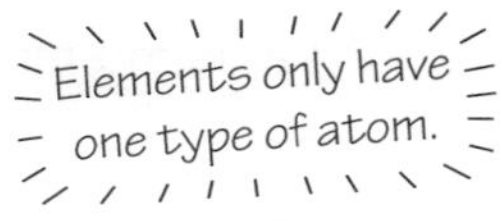

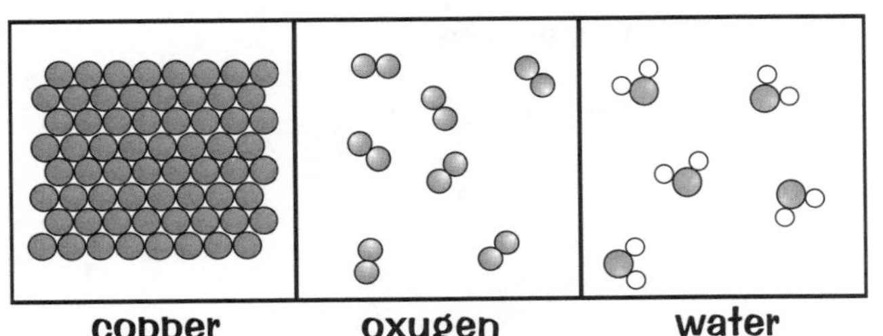

Q4 The diagrams below aren't finished. Write down how many **electrons** each atom should have.

a)

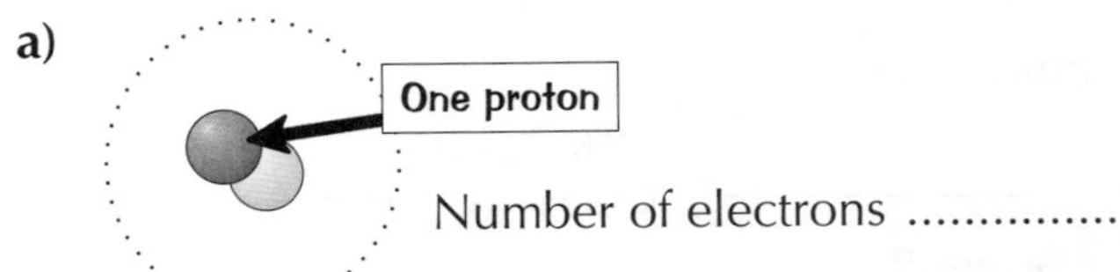

b)

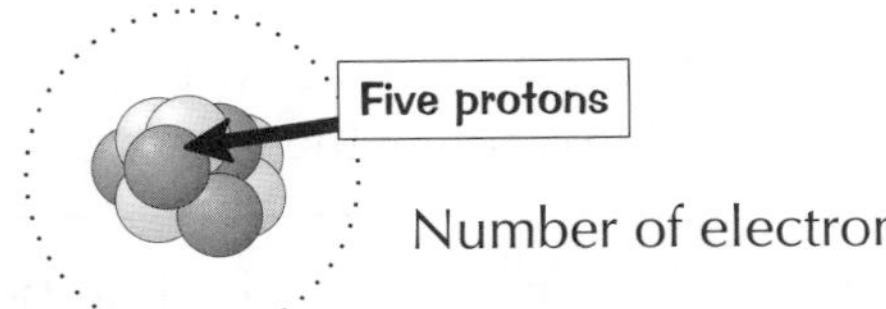

Number of electrons ....

c)

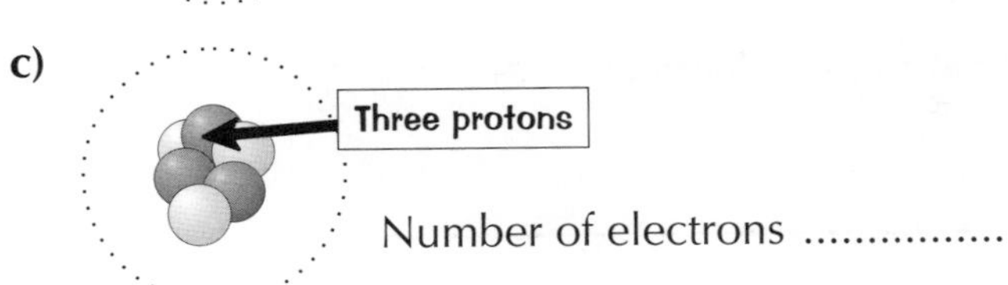

d)

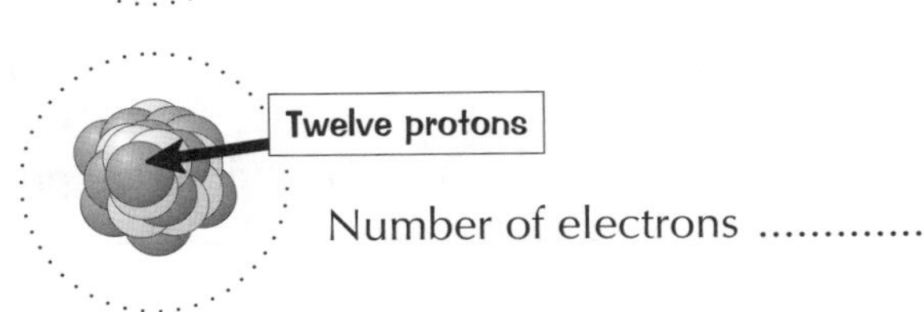

The Periodic Table

Q1 One of the diagrams below shows a **group** in the periodic table. Circle the one that does.

A

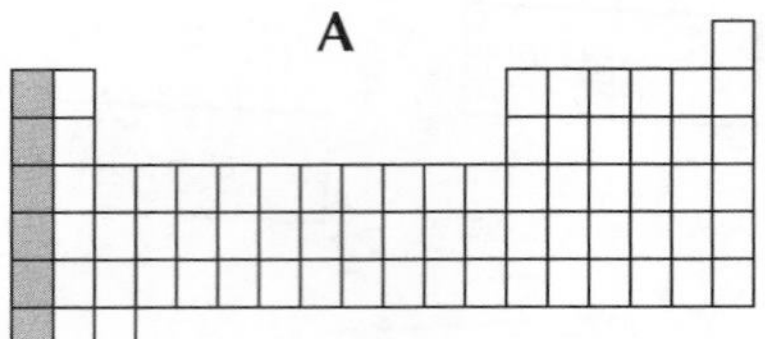

B

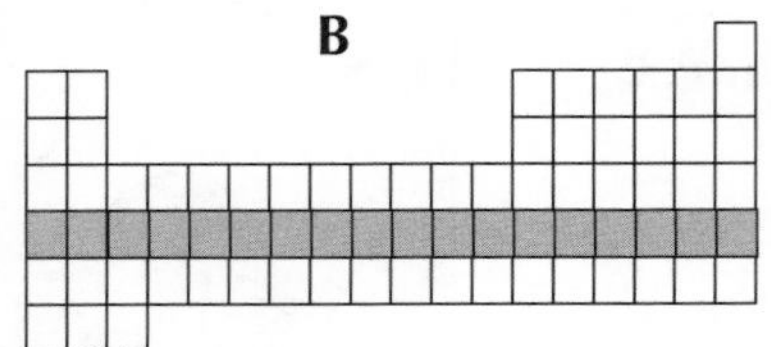

C

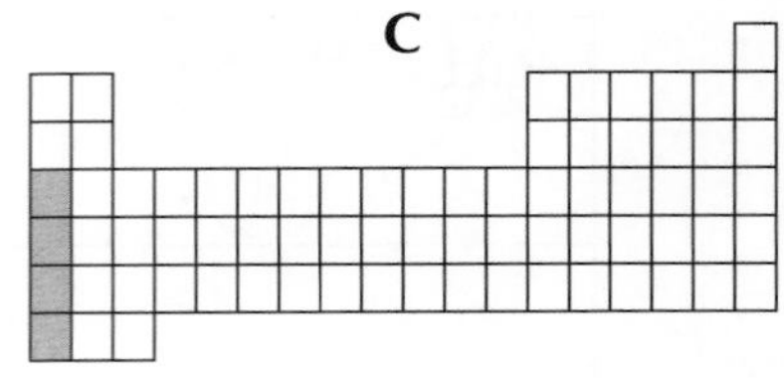

Q2 Are these sentences **true** or **false**? Tick the boxes.

		True	False
a)	The noble gases are in Group 1.	☐	☐
b)	C is the symbol for oxygen.	☐	☐
c)	Each element has a one or two letter symbol.	☐	☐

Q3 The diagram shows how **sodium** is shown in the periodic table.

$^{23}_{11}\text{Na}$

a) Circle the **atomic number** on the diagram.

b) How many **protons** does sodium have? ....

Q4 What is the **mass number** of an element? Tick the box.

☐ The total number of neutrons and electrons.

☐ The total number of protons and neutrons.

☐ The total number of protons and electrons.

Q5 Elements in the **same group** have **similar properties**.

Look at the periodic table on the inside front cover of this book to help you.

a) Tick the pair of elements that has similar properties.

A potassium and rubidium ☐ **B** helium and fluorine ☐

b) Sodium and potassium react with water in a similar way.
Circle the right words in the sentences below.

One has been done for you.

Sodium and potassium are both in (**Group 1**) / **Group 2**.

This means they have the same number of **neutrons / electrons** in their outer shell.

This gives them **similar / different** properties.

Electron Shells

Q1 Are these sentences **true** or **false**? Tick the boxes.

	True	False
a) In atoms, electrons can be found in shells.	☐	☐
b) Atoms with full outer shells will react.	☐	☐
c) The first shell can only have 2 electrons.	☐	☐

Q2 Fluorine has **9 protons**.

a) How many electrons does fluorine have? ....

b) Draw these electrons onto the **shells** in the diagram below.
Draw a cross (X) to show each electron.

c) How many more electrons could the outer shell take? Circle your answer.

1 0 7

Q3 Write out the **electronic structure** for the elements below.
The number of electrons in each element is given in brackets.

Beryllium (4 electrons) ....2, 2...............

a) Oxygen (8 electrons) ....

b) Magnesium (12 electrons) ....

c) Silicon (14 electrons) ....

One has been done for you.

Q4 Circle the right words in the sentences below.

Atoms are much happier when they have a full **inner shell / outer shell**. It means they **won't / will** react. For example, the noble gases all have full outer shells — so they're **reactive / unreactive**.

Electron Shells

Q5 **Chlorine** has 17 protons.

Remember — the number of protons is the same as the number of electrons.

a) What is its electronic structure? .... , ... , ...

b) Draw the electrons on the shells in the diagram. Use a cross (X) for each electron.

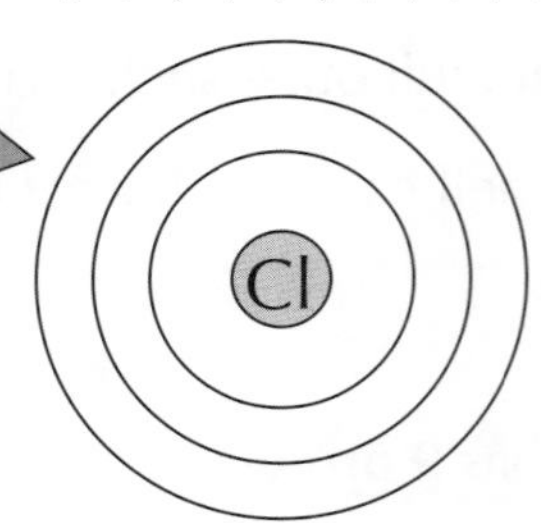

c) How many shells are **full** in a chlorine atom?

....

Q6 Draw the **full electronic structures** for these elements. (The first two have been done for you.)

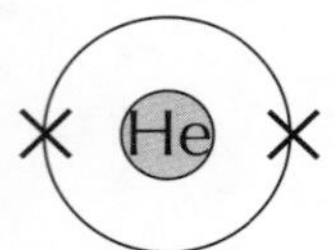

Helium (2 electrons)

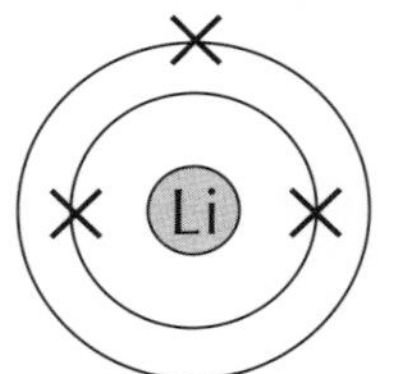

Lithium (3 electrons)

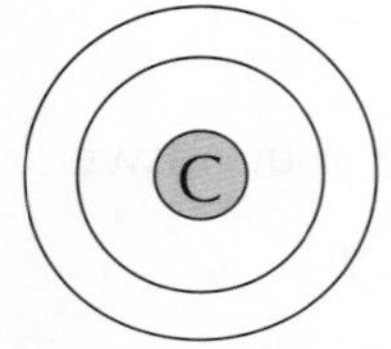

a) Carbon (6 electrons)

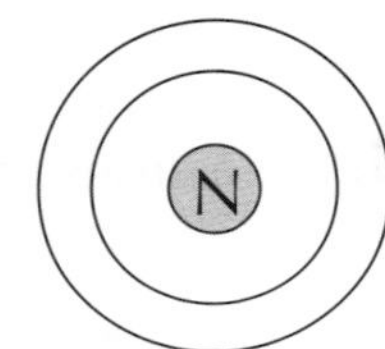

b) Nitrogen (7 electrons)

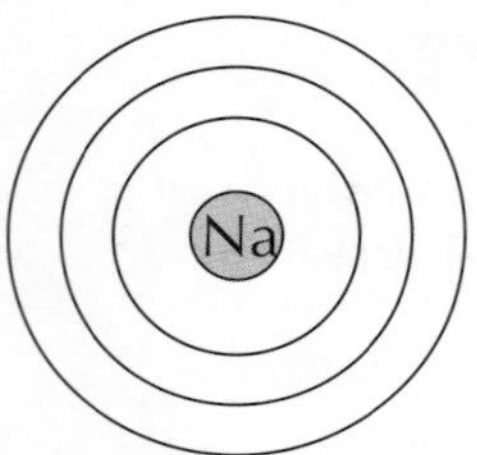

c) Sodium (11 electrons)

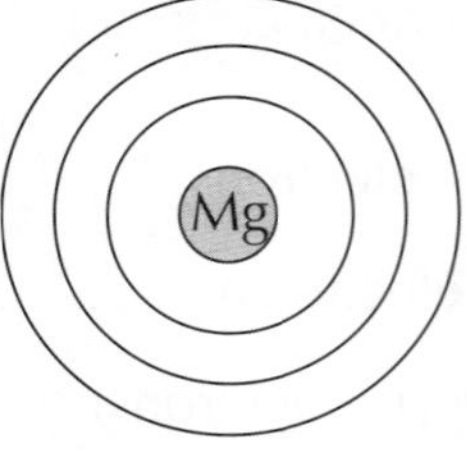

d) Magnesium (12 electrons)

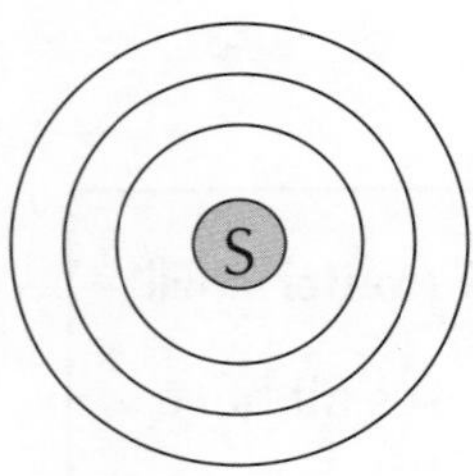

e) Sulfur (16 electrons)

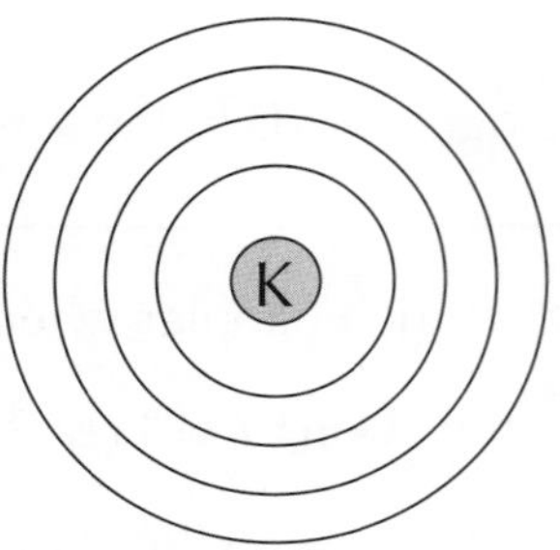

f) Potassium (19 electrons)

Compounds and Chemical Reactions

Q1 Are these sentences **true** or **false**? Tick the boxes.

	True	False
a) Atoms can react with other atoms to make compounds.	☐	☐
b) Atoms can give and take protons to make compounds.	☐	☐
c) Atoms can share electrons to make a covalent bond.	☐	☐

Q2 a) Draw lines to match the type of compound to what it's made from.

Compound made from a non-metal and a metal — ions

Compound made from two non-metals — molecules

b) Which of these sentences is **true**? Tick the box.

Metals lose electrons to form negative ions. ☐
Metals lose electrons to form positive ions. ☐

Q3 The **symbol equation** shows the reaction between calcium and oxygen.

$$2Ca + O_2 \rightarrow 2CaO$$

Ca Ca   O O   Ca O   Ca O

a) How many atoms of calcium were there at the start of the reaction? ....

b) How many atoms of oxygen were there at the start of the reaction? ....

c) Circle the right word in the sentence below.

Atoms **are / aren't** lost or made in a chemical reaction.

d) At the **start** of the reaction there were **10 g of reactants**.
What **mass of products** would there be at the **end** of the reaction?

....

Limestone

Q1 What is **limestone** mainly made of? Circle the answer.

sodium carbonate   calcium hydroxide   calcium carbonate

Q2 **Carbonates** break down when heated.

a) Limestone is a carbonate. Name the two products made when limestone is heated.

1. ....

2. ....

b) What has happened to the carbonate? Tick the answer.

It has been neutralised. ☐   It has been thermally decomposed. ☐

It has been cracked. ☐

c) Can you break down all carbonates using a Bunsen burner? Circle the answer.

Yes   No

Q3 Circle the right words in the sentences below.

Calcium carbonate reacts with **acid / salt**. This reaction means that statues made of limestone (calcium carbonate) can be damaged by **carbon dioxide / acid rain**.

Q4 Magnesium carbonate will react with an acid to make a **salt**.

a) Give the **two other** things that are made in this reaction.

1. ....

2. ....

b) Name **two other** metal carbonates that will react with an acid.

1. ....

2. ....

Limestone

Q5 Calcium oxide reacts with water to make **calcium hydroxide**.

a) Complete the word equation to show this reaction.

calcium oxide + ... → ....

b) Calcium hydroxide is an alkali. What would it do to an acid? Circle the answer.

make it more acidic   turn it into limestone   neutralise it

Q6 Calcium hydroxide is also called **limewater**.

a) What gas is limewater used to test for? Circle the answer.

sulfur dioxide   carbon dioxide   oxygen

b) What happens when this gas is bubbled through limewater?
Fill in the diagram with words from the box.

goes cloudy
goes colourless
goes orange

gas

calcium hydroxide

....

Q7 Complete the equations to show how **cement**, **mortar** and **concrete** are made. Use words from the box.

sand   clay   water   gravel

You'll need to use some of the words more than once.

a) limestone + ... → cement

b) cement + ... + ... → mortar

c) cement + ... + ... + ... → concrete

Q8 Circle **two advantages** of **quarrying** limestone.

Less noise   Makes more jobs   Gives us limestone for building houses

Quarries are good homes for birds and animals   More tourists

Getting Metals from Rocks

Q1 Circle the right words in the sentences below.

Metals like gold are **reactive / unreactive**. They can be found on their own in the ground.

Other metals are reactive. They form **elements / compounds** with other things in the ground.

Compounds with a lot of metal in them are called **ores / rocks**.

Q2 Metals can be **extracted**.

a) What does this mean? Tick the box next to the answer.

- [ ] Extraction means getting metals out of ores.
- [ ] Extraction means making ores from metal.

b) Number the boxes below **1-4** to show how metals can be extracted.

The first one has been done for you.

☐ **Metal is purified.**

☐ **Metal ore is concentrated.**

1 **Metal ore is mined.**

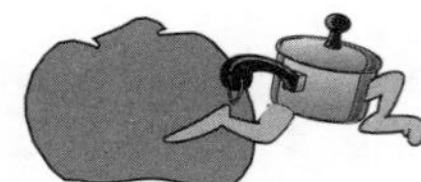

☐ **Metal is extracted with a chemical reaction.**

Q3 **Carbon** can be used to extract some metals.

a) Using carbon to extract metals takes away oxygen. What is this called? Circle the right word.

oxidation   reduction   decomposition

b) Iron can be extracted from iron oxide using carbon.
Complete the word equation for the reaction.

iron oxide + ... → .... + carbon dioxide

c) Some metals are above carbon in the reactivity series. How are these extracted?
Circle the answer.

with carbon   by electrolysis   with heat

Getting Metals from Rocks

Q4 Copper is found in the ground in **ores**.

a) How is copper **extracted** from the ores? Circle the answer.

It's heated with carbon. | It's cooled to below its freezing point. | It's mixed with pure copper and left overnight.

b) Circle the process that's used to **purify** the extracted copper.

evaporation | filtration | electrolysis

Q5 Add the labels in the box to the diagram of **electrolysis** below.

positive ions	negative ions

a) .... **b)** ....

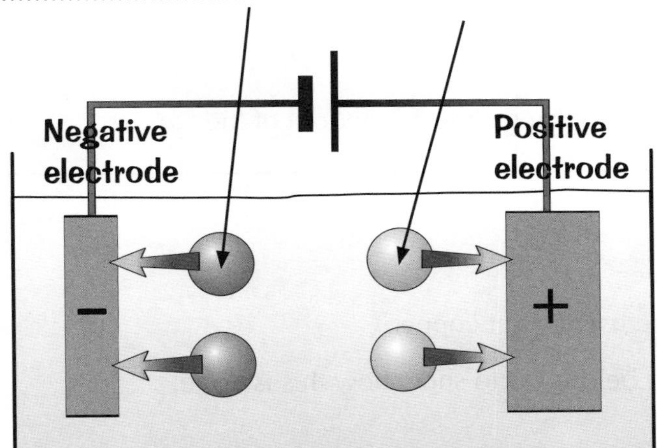

Q6 Aluminium is extracted using **electrolysis**.

a) This is **expensive**. Tick the **two** reasons why.

- ☐ Ions are expensive.
- ☐ There are lots of stages in the process.
- ☐ A lot of energy is needed.
- ☐ Aluminium is very heavy.

b) Aluminium **can't** be extracted using **carbon**. Why not?

....

Getting Metals from Rocks

Q7 Circle the right words in the sentences below.

A reactive metal will replace a **less / more** reactive metal in a solution. Iron is **less / more** reactive than copper. So, you can get copper from a solution using **iron / more copper**.

Q8 **Phytomining** can be used to get copper from the soil.

Fill in the gaps in the passage using some of the words in the box.

ash	air	soil	copper

Plants are grown in .... that has copper in it.

The plants take up the ....

The plants are burnt. You get the copper out of the ....

Q9 **Bioleaching** can be used to get copper.

a) Number the boxes below **1-3** to show how this is done.

☐ This makes a solution that has copper in it.

☐ Bacteria are used to get the copper from its ore.

☐ You can then get the copper out of the solution.

b) Is bioleaching better or worse for the **environment** than normal mining?

....

Impacts of Extracting Metals

Q1 Mining has **advantages** and **disadvantages**.
Put the sentences about mining in the table below.

One has been done for you.

It destroys the homes of birds and animals. It's ugly and noisy.

It makes jobs in the mine. People can fall down old mines.

It brings money into the area. It ~~gives us metals to make things~~ with.

ADVANTAGES OF MINING ✓	DISADVANTAGES OF MINING ✗
It gives us metals to make things with.	

Q2 **Recycling** metals is important.

a) Which of the following are **good reasons** for recycling metals? Tick **two** boxes.

- ☐ Recycled metals are much shinier.
- ☐ Recycling uses less energy and less fossil fuels.
- ☐ Recycling saves money.
- ☐ Recycling metals is less noisy than mining.

b) Give **two** more reasons why it's important to recycle metals.

1. ....

2. ....

Properties of Metals

Q1 All **metals** share some properties.

a) Circle the properties that **all** metals share.

strong bendy don't conduct heat

weak don't conduct electricity

stiff conduct heat conduct electricity

b) What are elements from the centre block of the periodic table called? Circle the answer.

alloys transition metals noble gases

Q2 **Copper** has lots of uses.

a) Circle **two** properties of copper that make it good for use in **plumbing**.

It's the right colour for pipes. It's really light.

It doesn't react with water. It can be bent but is still hard.

b) Give **one** property of copper that makes it useful for **electrical wiring**.

....

Q3 This table shows the **properties** of three different **metals**.

When a metal corrodes it reacts with water and air. This damages it.

Metal	Heat conduction	Cost	Does it corrode?	Strength
1	average	high	no	good
2	average	medium	not much	excellent
3	excellent	low	not much	good

Choose which metal would be **best** for making each of the following:

a) Saucepan bases ....

b) Car bodies ....

c) A statue to be placed in a town centre ....

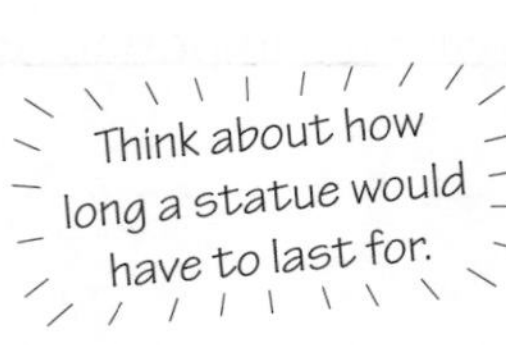

Alloys

Q1 Circle the right words in the sentences below.

> Iron made in a blast furnace is **96% / 100%** iron.
>
> It's called **pure iron / cast iron**.
>
> It doesn't have many uses because it's **bendy / brittle**.

Q2 Most iron is made into the alloy **steel**.

Are these sentences **true** or **false**? Tick the boxes.

		True	False
a)	An alloy can be a mixture of two metals.	☐	☐
b)	An alloy is never a mixture of a metal and a non-metal.	☐	☐
c)	Steels are mixtures of iron and carbon.	☐	☐
d)	Alloys aren't as useful as pure metals.	☐	☐

Q3 a) Draw lines to join the **metals and alloys** to their **properties**.

One has been done for you.

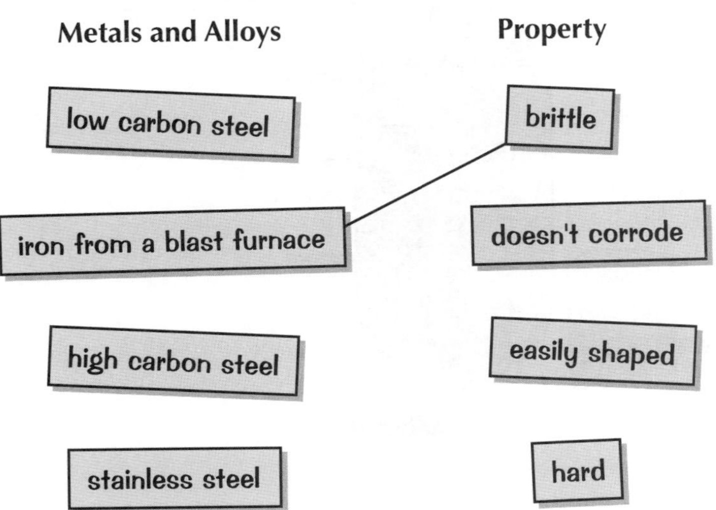

b) Circle the right words in the sentences below.

> Gold is too **soft / hard** for most uses.
>
> It can be mixed with other metals to make a **softer / harder** alloy.

Fractional Distillation of Crude Oil

Q1 Circle the right words in the sentences below.

a) Crude oil is made up of a **mixture** / **fraction** of lots of compounds.
These compounds are mostly **carbohydrates** / **hydrocarbons**.

b) Hydrocarbons are made of carbon and **hydrogen** / **helium** atoms only.

c) In a mixture there are **some** / **no** chemical bonds between the substances.

Q2 The diagram shows how **crude oil** is split up by **fractional distillation**.

Add the labels to the diagram by putting the letters in the boxes.

A The fractions are collected at different levels.

B Heated crude oil is piped in at the bottom.

C The oil evaporates and rises up the column.

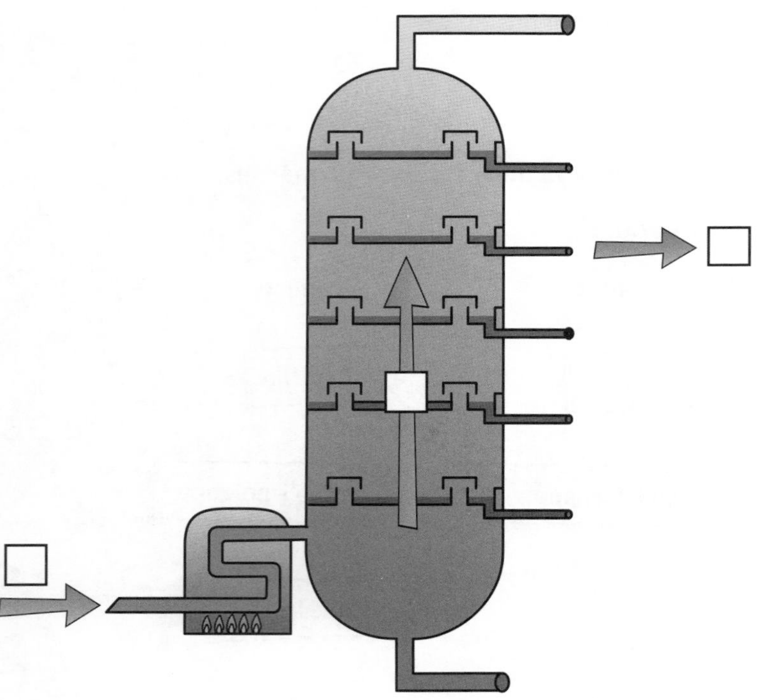

Q3 Fractions are **groups** of hydrocarbons.

What is similar about hydrocarbons in the same fraction? Tick the box next to the answer.

They have similar numbers of carbon atoms. ☐

They all have the same number of hydrogen atoms. ☐

Properties and Uses of Crude Oil

Q1 Alkanes can be shown with a **formula**.

Write down how many carbon and hydrogen atoms are in each formula below.

a) C_2H_6

carbon atoms ....

hydrogen atoms ....

b) C_3H_8

carbon atoms ....

hydrogen atoms ....

Q2 a) Tick the box next to the **general formula** for **alkanes**.

☐ C_nH ☐ C_nH_{2n+2} ☐ $C_{3n}H_{2n+4}$

b) Below are the first three alkanes.
Draw lines to match the structures to their names.

```
    H
    |
H — C — H
    |
    H
```

```
    H   H
    |   |
H — C — C — H
    |   |
    H   H
```

```
    H   H   H
    |   |   |
H — C — C — C — H
    |   |   |
    H   H   H
```

Ethane **Propane** **Methane**

c) Circle the right word in the sentence below.

Alkanes are **saturated / unsaturated** hydrocarbons.

Q3 **Long** hydrocarbons have different **properties** from **short hydrocarbons**.
Fill in the table using the properties in the box below.

One has been done for you.

~~runny~~ hard to set on fire low boiling point high boiling point viscous flammable

LONG HYDROCARBON	SHORT HYDROCARBON
	runny

Using Crude Oil as a Fuel

Q1 Circle the right words in the sentences below.

Extracting crude oil is a **small** / **big** industry.

Crude oil fractions make good **fuels** / **salad dressings**.

Q2 Crude oil is **non-renewable**.

a) What does **non-renewable** mean? Tick the right box.

☐ If something is non-renewable it will run out one day.

☐ If something is non-renewable there will always be more of it.

b) What could we do about the fact that crude oil is non-renewable? Circle **three** answers.

make more crude oil

use as much crude oil as we can

find new fuels

use less crude oil

stop using crude oil for transport

c) Will crude oil get cheaper or more expensive in the future?

....

d) Why would it be difficult to suddenly start using a different fuel? Tick the answer.

Everything is nicely set up for using crude oil. ☐

There would be too much crude oil left. ☐

There aren't any other fuels we could use. ☐

Q3 **Burning** crude oil and **carrying** it across the sea in boats can be bad for the environment. Complete the table to give some reasons why.

Burning crude oil	Carrying crude oil across the sea in boats
1. causes global dimming	1. oil spills poison sea creatures
2.	2. ....
3.	

Environmental Problems

Q1 We burn a lot of **hydrocarbons** in everyday life.

a) Circle the word below that means 'burning fuels'.

combustion   neutralisation   thermal decomposition

b) Circle the right words in the sentence.

Burning hydrocarbons **takes in / gives out** heat.

Q2 Burning hydrocarbons can give off **solid particles**.

What can solid particles contain? Tick **two** of the boxes.

fuel that hasn't burnt ☐   litter ☐   oxides of nitrogen ☐   soot ☐

Q3 Burning hydrocarbons also gives off **gases**.

The diagram below shows some of these gases. Fill in the last two labels.

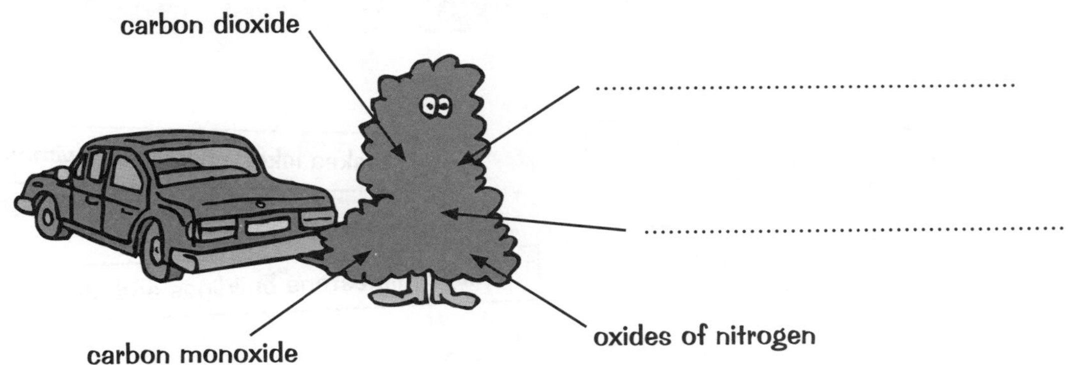

Q4 Match the **type of burning** to the **amount of oxygen** and the **gas given off**. Draw lines between the boxes.

Type of burning	Amount of oxygen	Gas given off
complete combustion	plenty of oxygen	carbon monoxide
partial combustion	not enough oxygen	carbon dioxide

Environmental Problems

Q5 Burning **fossil fuels** gives off **gases**.

Draw lines to link the parts of these sentences.

If you burn a fuel that has sulfur in it you'll get...	...oxides of nitrogen.
If the fuel you burn gets hot enough you'll get...	...sulfur dioxide.

Q6 Burning **fossil fuels** causes **acid rain**.

a) Add the labels to the diagram below. Write the letters in the boxes.

A — acid rain B — acid cloud C — sulfur dioxide and oxides of nitrogen D — ~~clean~~ cloud

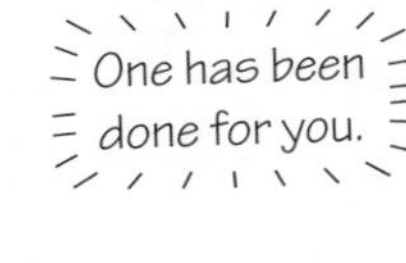

b) Circle **two** problems that acid rain causes.

kills plants, animals and trees

makes lakes unsafe for swimming

causes volcanoes

damages limestone buildings and statues

Q7 There are ways we can help **stop acid rain**.

a) How can we do this? Tick the box next to the answer.

We can take sulfur out of fuels before we burn them in our cars.	☐
We can filter rain as it falls from the sky to get rid of the acid.	☐
We can remove the acid from the clouds using carbon.	☐

b) Give **one other way** that we can help stop acid rain.

Think about power stations.

....

More Environmental Problems

Q1 Circle the right words in the sentences below.

Global dimming is caused by **particles / carbon dioxide.**

Global dimming means **less light / more light** is reaching the Earth.

Q2 Look at the graph and then answer the questions below.

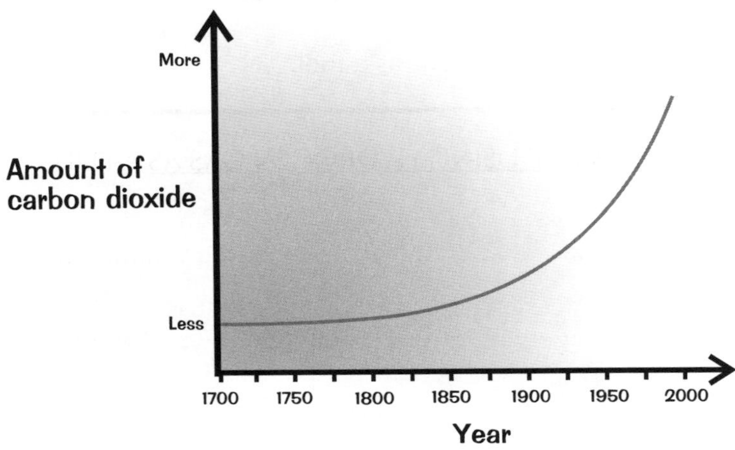

a) What has happened to the amount of carbon dioxide over the years? Circle the answer.

It has gone up. **It has stayed the same.** **It has gone down.**

b) Why has this happened? Tick the box next to the answer.

- We are burning lots of hydrogen gas. ☐
- We are burning lots of fossil fuels. ☐
- We have heated too much limestone. ☐

Q3 The Earth is **warming up**.

a) What is this called?

....

b) Why is the Earth warming up? Tick the box next to the answer.

☐ **Extra carbon dioxide is trapping heat.**

☐ **There is less carbon dioxide to cool the Earth down.**

More Environmental Problems

Q4 **Hydrogen gas** can be used to power a car engine.

a) What is given off when hydrogen gas is **used in an engine**? Tick the answer.

just carbon dioxide ☐ just water ☐ carbon dioxide and water ☐

b) Circle the right word in the sentence below.

Hydrogen gas **will / won't** run out.

c) Give **three disadvantages** of using hydrogen gas as a fuel.

DISADVANTAGES OF USING HYDROGEN GAS AS A FUEL:

1. ....

2. ....

3. ....

Barry 4 Karen

Think about where it comes from, the engine it needs and how it's stored.

Q5 **Ethanol** can be used as a fuel.

a) Circle the right words in the sentences below.

Ethanol can be made from **plants / gases** and used as a fuel.

However, this means there are **more / fewer** plants for food.

There are advantages though. Burning ethanol doesn't give off **carbon dioxide / sulfur dioxide**. Also, ethanol **will / won't** run out.

b) Do you need a special engine to run a car on ethanol? Circle the answer.

yes no

Mixed Questions — Chemistry 1a

Q1 All **metals** are the same in some ways.

a) Where are **metals** found on the periodic table? Tick the box.

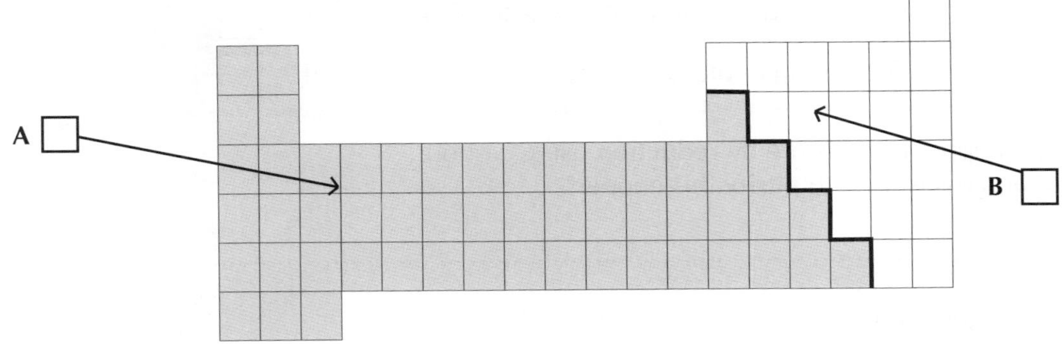

b) Tick the sentences that are **true**.

☐ Metals are strong (hard to break).

☐ No metals corrode.

☐ Metals are great at conducting electricity.

☐ Metals are bad at conducting heat.

☐ A metal can be made more useful by turning it into an alloy.

c) Circle the right word in the sentence.

Alloys like steel are **harder** / **softer** than pure metals.

Q2 Look at the information in the table below.

R, S, T and U are all metals.

Metal	Strength	Weight
R	Strong	Light
S	Quite Strong	Quite Light
T	Strong	Quite Heavy
U	Weak	Heavy

a) Which metal would be the best for building an **aeroplane**? ....

b) Give two reasons for your answer.

1. ....

2. ....

Mixed Questions — Chemistry 1a

Q3 You can get the metals **aluminium** and **copper** from their ores.

a) Tick the sentence that is **true**.

There is a set amount of metals in the Earth. ☐

There is an endless amount of metals in the Earth. ☐

b) You get copper from its ore by **reduction** using carbon.
What process is used to **purify** this copper?

....

c) You can't get aluminium from its ore using carbon.
Circle the method that is used instead.

phytomining | electrolysis | bioleaching

Q4 **Petrol** and **diesel** are used as fuels.

a) Diesel is made of **long hydrocarbons**. Petrol is made of **short hydrocarbons**.
Complete the list below to show the **properties** of petrol.

Don't think of them as petrol and diesel. Think of them as short and long hydrocarbons.

DIESEL	PETROL
Viscous	1. ....
High boiling point	2. ....
Hard to set on fire	3. ....

b) Ethanol, hydrogen gas and biodiesel can be used as fuels.
Fill in the table by writing '**yes**' or '**no**'.

One has been done for you.

Fuel	Does it need a special engine?	Does burning it release carbon dioxide?
Ethanol		Yes
Hydrogen gas		
Biodiesel		

Mixed Questions — Chemistry 1a

Q5 Argon has an **atomic number** of 18.

a) How many electrons does argon have? ....

b) Draw these electrons onto the **shells** in the diagram to the right.
Use a cross (X) for each electron.

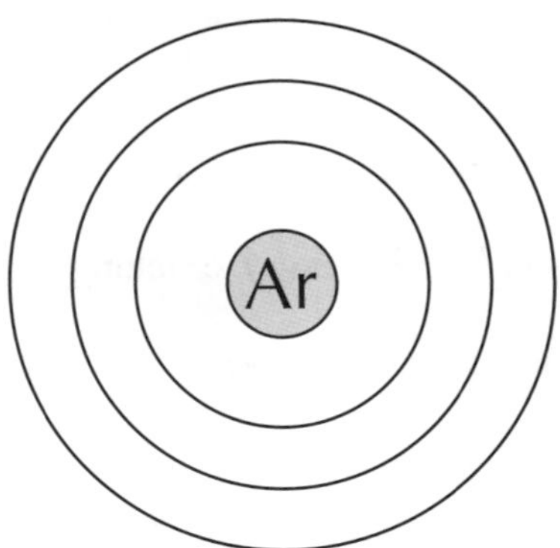

Q6 **Limestone** (calcium carbonate) has many uses.

a) **Calcium carbonate** can be turned into **calcium hydroxide**.
Use **one** of the labels from the box to complete the equation below.

hydrogen | calcium oxide | carbon dioxide | limewater

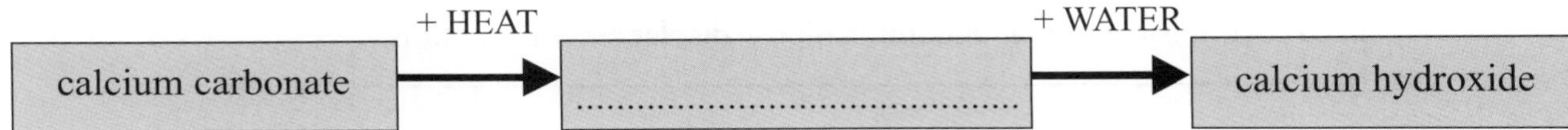

b) Limestone can be made into other things.
Complete the diagram using the words in the box.

cement | concrete

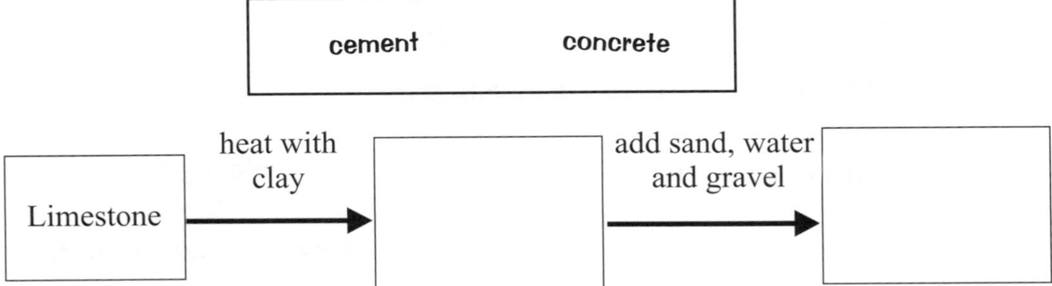

Q7 The limestone of the Houses of Parliament is crumbling away.

a) What is causing the damage to the limestone? Circle the answer.

acid rain | global dimming | global warming

b) Give **one** way that we could reduce this problem.

....

Cracking Crude Oil

Q1 Circle the right words in the sentences.

Long hydrocarbons can be turned into **shorter / longer** ones.

This is called **filtering / cracking**.

The shorter hydrocarbons are called alkanes and **emulsions / alkenes**.

These are **more / less** useful.

Q2 The hydrocarbons you get from **cracking** have lots of uses.

a) What can some of the hydrocarbons be used as? Circle the answer.

catalysts   fuels   food

b) Circle the right word(s) in the sentence below.

Cracking is a **thermal decomposition / displacement** reaction.

Q3 Hydrocarbons can be **cracked** in the lab.

a) The diagram shows how hydrocarbons are cracked.
Label the diagram by writing A, B and C in the boxes.

A The long hydrocarbon breaks down into short alkanes and alkenes.

B The long hydrocarbon is heated so that it turns into a gas.

C The gas is passed over a hot catalyst.

b) What is **another way** of cracking hydrocarbons? Tick the box next to the answer.

☐ Heat the hydrocarbon so it turns into a gas. Then mix the gas with steam at a very high temperature.

☐ Mix the hydrocarbon with water. Then pass it over a hot catalyst.

Alkenes and Ethanol

Q1 What is the general **formula** for an alkene? Tick the right box.

Q2 Complete this table with the names of the alkenes.

Name of alkene	Formula
a)	$H_2C=CH_2$
b)	$CH_3-CH=CH_2$

Q3 You can test for alkenes by adding them to **bromine water**.

Circle the right words in the sentence.

> An alkene will turn the bromine water from **orange / green** to **yellow / colourless**.

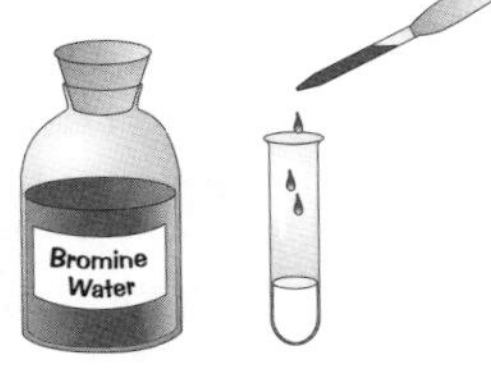

Q4 Are these sentences **true** or **false**? Tick the boxes.

	True	False
a) Alkenes have single bonds between all the carbon atoms.	☐	☐
b) Alkenes are unsaturated.	☐	☐
c) Ethene can be used to make ethanol.	☐	☐

Alkenes and Ethanol

Q5 There are two ways of making ethanol:

Method A	sugar → ethanol + carbon dioxide
Method B	ethene + steam → ethanol

a) Which one of the methods is called **fermentation**? ....

b) Draw lines to match the method to the process.

Method A — Uses a catalyst

Method B — Uses yeast

c) There are **advantages** to making ethanol from sugar.
Tick the box next to **one** advantage.

- Ethanol made from sugar is free. ☐
- Ethanol made from sugar is a cheap fuel. ☐
- Ethanol made from sugar has more uses than ethanol made from ethene. ☐

Q6 Some things are **renewable** and some things are **non-renewable**.

a) Draw lines to match the words to the correct meanings.

Renewable — Will run out

Non-renewable — Won't run out

b) Ethene comes from **crude oil**. Circle the right word in the sentence below.

Crude oil is **renewable** / **non-renewable**.

c) Ethanol can be made from **ethene** or from **sugar**.
Which method uses **renewable** substances? Circle the answer.

making ethanol from ethene   making ethanol from sugar

Using Alkenes to Make Polymers

Q1 Draw lines to match the **alkene** to the **polymer** it makes.

Alkene	Polymer
Ethene	Poly(propene)
Propene	Poly(ethene)

Q2 Add the labels from the box to the diagram below.

polymer monomers

```
H     H   H     H
 C=C       C=C
H     H   H     H

H     H   H     H
 C=C       C=C
H     H   H     H
```

→

```
   H H H H H H H H
   | | | | | | | |
 — C-C-C-C-C-C-C-C —
   | | | | | | | |
   H H H H H H H H
```

a) .... b) ....

Q3 Look at the list of things below. Circle the **one** thing polymers **can't** be used to make.

tooth fillings ethanol mattresses made of memory foam

biodegradable plastic bags plasters

Q4 It's important to **recycle polymers**.

Circle the right words in the sentences.

Most polymers **will / won't** rot. They aren't biodegradable.

This means they'll still be there **days later / years later**.

Alkenes for making polymers come from **the air / crude oil**.

This **is / isn't** running out.

Q5 Scientists are making new plastic bags that **can biodegrade**.

What are they making them from? Circle the answer.

cornstarch and ethanol polymers and metals polymers and cornstarch

Plant Oils

Q1 Olive oil can be removed from **olives**.

The method is written in the wrong order. Number the boxes **1-3** to put it in the right order.

☐ Water and other unwanted things are removed.

☐ The olives are crushed to make olive mush.

☐ The oil is pressed out of the mush.

Q2 There are two pairs of sentences below. Tick the sentence that is **true** in each pair.

a) ☐ Vegetable oils don't give us much energy.

☐ Vegetable oils give us a lot of energy.

b) ☐ Vegetable oils give us nutrients.

☐ Vegetable oils don't give us any nutrients.

Q3 Are these sentences **true** or **false**? Tick the boxes.

	True	False
a) Vegetable oils help food cook faster and at higher temperatures.	☐	☐
b) Cooking with vegetable oils gives food less energy.	☐	☐
c) Cooking food in oil doesn't change its flavour.	☐	☐

Q4 Vegetable oils aren't just used for **cooking**.

a) Use the words below to fill in the gaps in the sentences.

fuels	energy

Vegetable oils have lots of .... in them.

This means they make great ....

b) Name **one** fuel that can be made from vegetable oil.

....

Plant Oils

Q5 Martin tested some oils with **bromine water** to see if they were **saturated** or **unsaturated**.

a) Draw lines to match the type of **oil** to the type of **bond**.

saturated — carbon=carbon double bond

unsaturated — no double bond

b) Martin tested three oils — **A**, **B** and **C**.
His table shows what happened to the **bromine water**.
Draw circles to show if each oil is saturated or unsaturated.

Oil	What happened to the bromine water?	Is the oil saturated or unsaturated?
A	Stayed orange	saturated / unsaturated
B	Changed from orange to colourless	saturated / unsaturated
C	Stayed orange	saturated / unsaturated

Q6 Eating a lot of some oils gives you **a higher risk of heart disease** than others.

a) Draw lines to match the type of **oil** with the **risk** of heart disease from eating it.

Saturated — Lower risk of heart disease

Unsaturated — Higher risk of heart disease

b) Circle the correct word in the sentence below.

Both saturated and unsaturated oils make food **more / less** fattening.

Emulsions

Q1 Lots of things are made of **emulsions**.

a) What is an **emulsion**? Tick the box next to the answer.

☐ An emulsion is lots of droplets of one liquid in another liquid.

☐ An emulsion is only made from oil.

b) How would you make an emulsion from oil and water? Circle the answer.

Shake them together. Heat them in a boiling tube.

c) Tick **two** things that are emulsions.

☐ moisturiser ☐ water ☐ ethanol ☐ paint

Q2 Circle the right words in the sentences below.

Oils **do / don't** dissolve in water.

Emulsions are **thicker / runnier** than water and oil.

Emulsions are **good / bad** at coating things.

Emulsions are **smooth / rough.**

Q3 Are these sentences **true** or **false**? Tick the boxes.

	True	False
a) Emulsions always want to separate out.	☐	☐
b) Emulsifiers are added to make emulsions separate out.	☐	☐
c) Emulsifiers make emulsions last longer.	☐	☐

Q4 **Emulsifiers** can be added to emulsions.

Give a **disadvantage** of adding emulsifiers to **food**.

....

Continental Drift

Q1 Below is a letter that **Wegener** might have written.
Use the words in the box below to fill in the gaps.

fossils	chunks	land bridges
continental drift	joined together	

Dear Mr Heinz,

I am writing to tell you about my idea of ....

I can explain why there are matching .... in different continents. The idea that there were once .... between these continents is total rubbish.

I think that millions of years ago the continents were ....

The Earth is made of .... that have split apart.

From,

Wegener :-)

Q2 Wegener had **reasons** for his idea.

Tick **two** of the boxes to show what his reasons were.

- He found lines in the ground that showed where the chunks had split apart. ☐
- He found matching fossils in different continents. ☐
- He could still see the glue from where the continents were once joined together. ☐
- He saw that the continents would fit together like a jigsaw. ☐

USA

Q3 Below are two different ideas about how **mountains** were made.

Write **W** in the box next to Wegener's idea.
Write **S** in the box next to what other scientists thought.

☐ The Earth shrunk and crinkled as it cooled down. This made the mountains.

☐ Mountains were made by chunks crashing together.

The Earth's Structure

Q1 The diagram shows the Earth's structure. Label the **crust**, **core** and **mantle**.

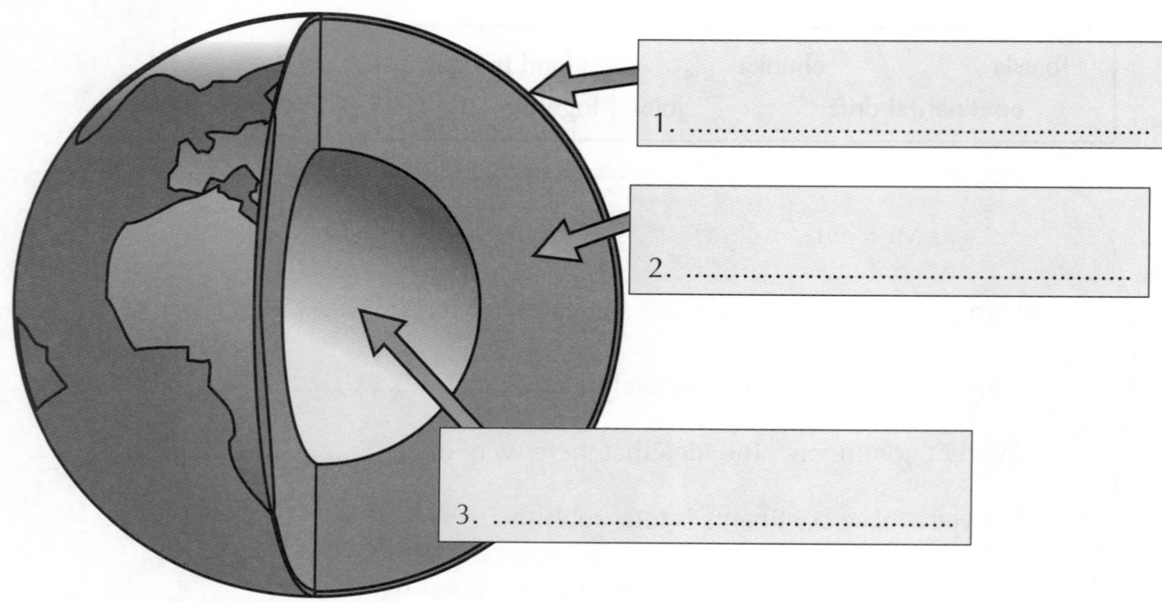

Q2 The map on the left shows where most of the world's **earthquakes** take place.
The map on the right shows the **tectonic plates**.

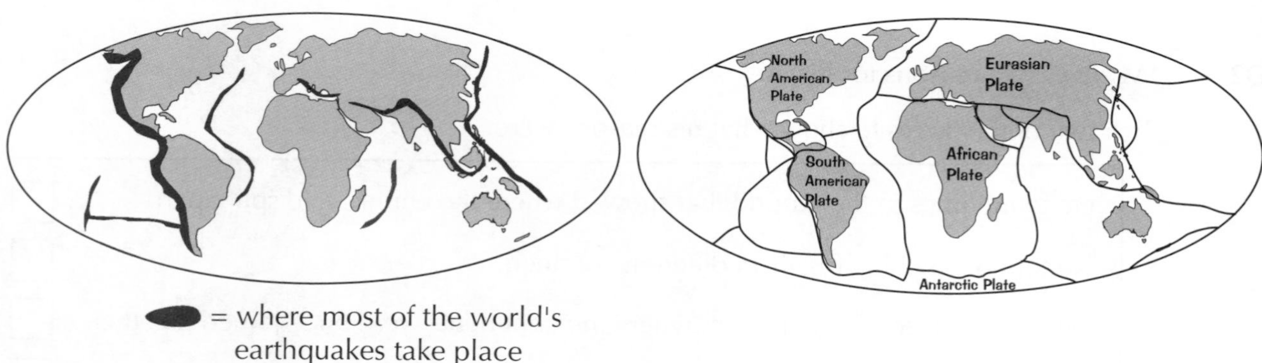

Compare the two maps. What do they tell you about where earthquakes happen?
Circle the answer.

Earthquakes never happen where two tectonic plates meet.

Earthquakes happen when things crash into the Earth.

Most earthquakes happen where two tectonic plates meet.

The Earth's Structure

Q3 Look at the diagram showing two tectonic plates.

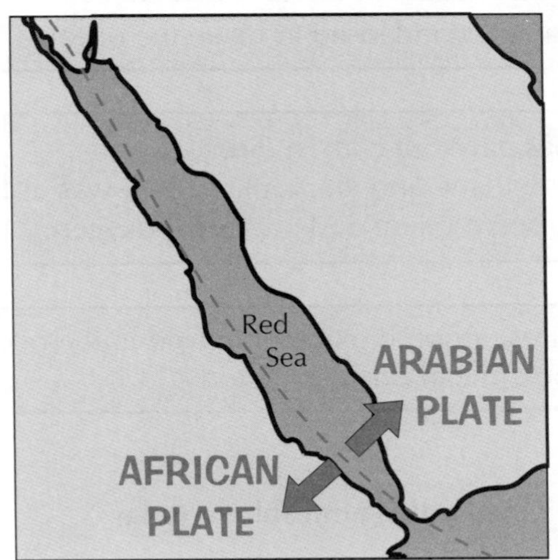

The two plates are moving apart by 16 mm per year.

How far apart will they move in 10 years?

....

.... mm

mm just stands for millimetres.

Q4 Match up the words to their description. One has been done for you.

Crust	Happen where plates meet
Mantle	Happen when plates suddenly jump forwards
Convection current	Caused by reactions giving off heat in the mantle
Tectonic plates	The outside of the Earth where we live
Earthquakes	Pieces of the crust that move very slowly
Volcanoes	The air that surrounds the Earth
Atmosphere	Moves around in convection currents

Q5 Tick the sentences below that are **true**.

- Tectonic plates can stay very still for a while and then suddenly jump forwards. ☐
- Tectonic plates move a few metres a year. ☐
- Earthquakes never happen where the plates meet. ☐
- We know exactly when earthquakes and volcanoes will happen. ☐
- Scientists don't know when volcanoes and earthquakes will happen. ☐

The Atmosphere

Q1 Draw lines to put the statements in the **right order** on the timeline. One has been done for you.

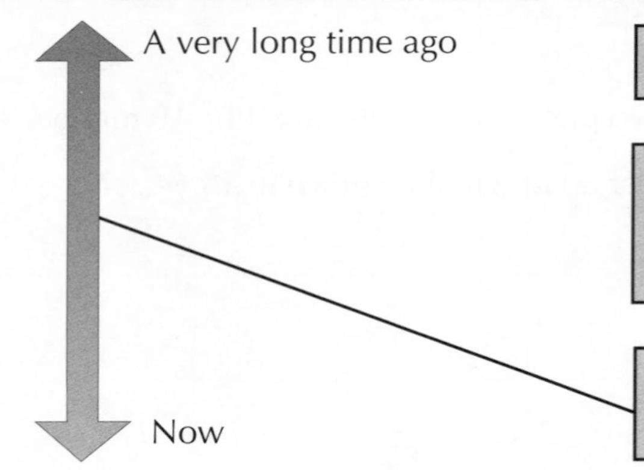

Water vapour condensed to make the oceans.

Volcanoes gave out carbon dioxide, water vapour, methane and ammonia. There was a lot of carbon dioxide and not much oxygen.

A lot of the carbon dioxide dissolved in the oceans. Plants took in carbon dioxide too.

Q2 This pie chart shows the amounts of different gases in the **Earth's atmosphere today**.

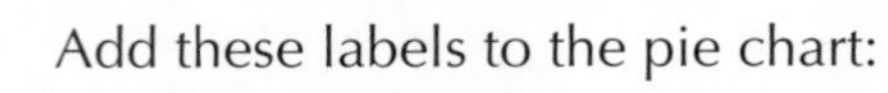

Add these labels to the pie chart: **nitrogen** **oxygen** **other gases**

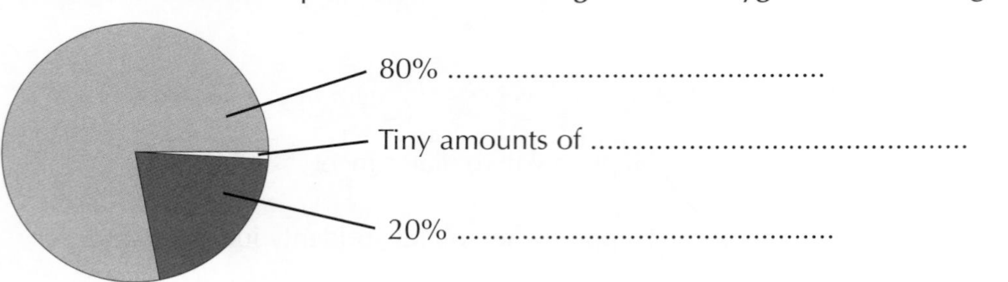

Q3 The amount of **carbon dioxide** in the atmosphere and the **temperature** of the Earth have changed over the years. The graphs show these changes.

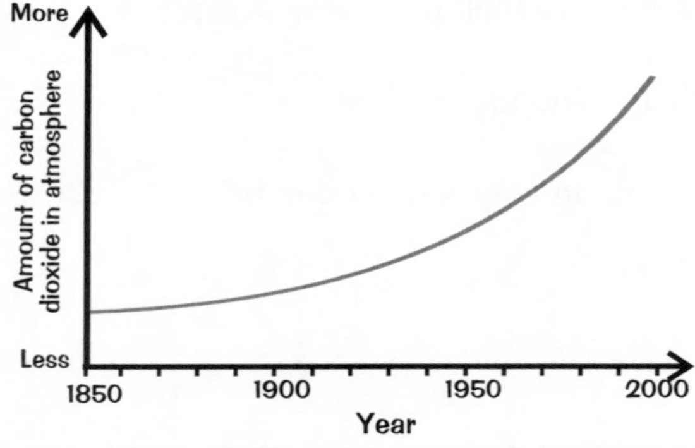

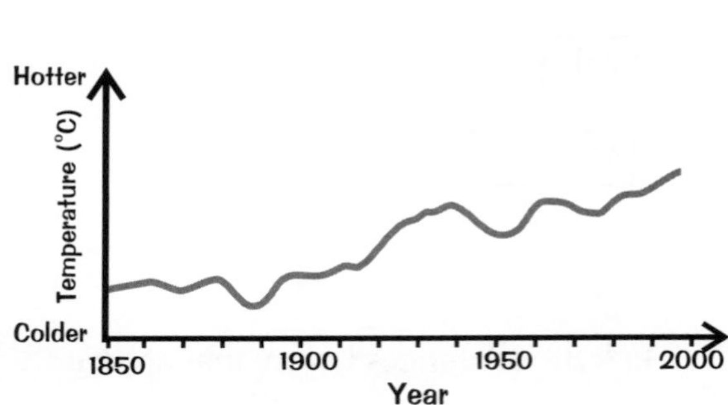

a) What is causing the amount of carbon dioxide to go up? Circle the answer.

cycling to work | photosynthesis | acid rain | burning fossil fuels

b) Has the temperature gone **up** or **down** between 1850 and 2000?

....

c) What is this temperature change known as? ....

Mixed Questions — Chemistry 1b

Q1 a) Look at the diagrams below and tick the one that shows **propene**.

H H H
H-C-C=C
H H ☐

H H H
H-C-C-C-H ☐
H H H

H H H H H H
—C-C-C=C-C-C-C-C— ☐
H H H H H H H H

b) Circle the right words in the sentences below.

Alkenes are **saturated / unsaturated.** They have **double / single** bonds.

Q2 The graphs give information about the Earth's atmosphere a long time ago and today.

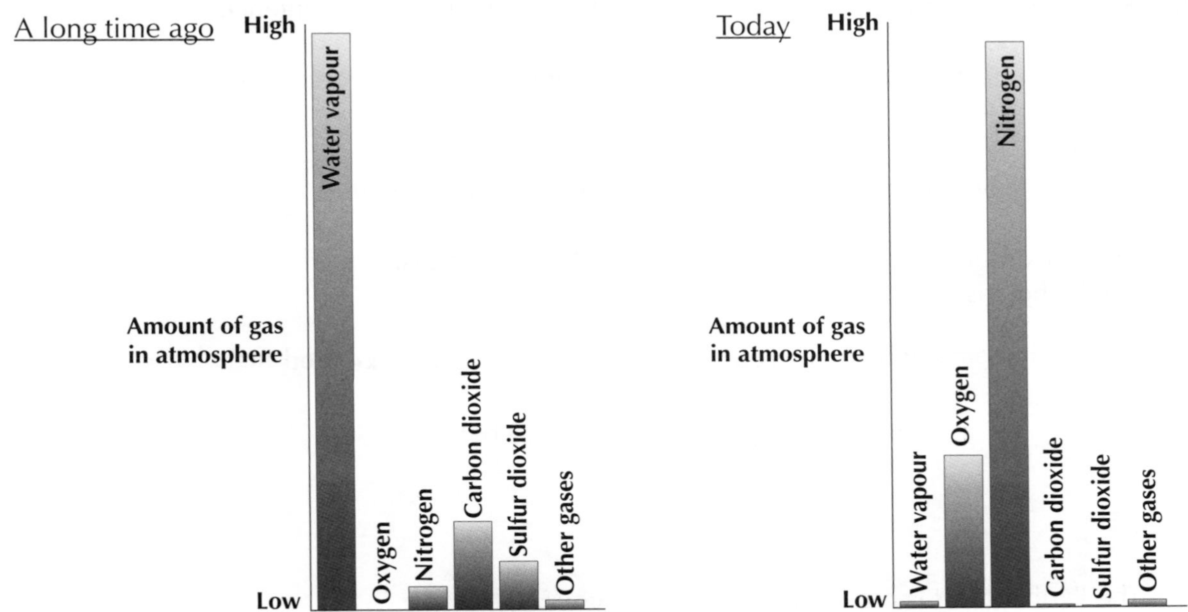

a) What removed carbon dioxide from the atmosphere and gave out oxygen? Circle the answer.

fossils **sea creatures** **plants** **volcanoes**

b) What has happened to the amount of nitrogen in the atmosphere?

....

c) Tick the boxes to show which sentences are **true**.

A small amount of the atmosphere today is noble gases.	☐
Volcanoes give out lots of gases.	☐
The amount of carbon dioxide is going up because humans are creating fossil fuels.	☐

Mixed Questions — Chemistry 1b

Q3 The **ingredients** list from a tin of **macaroni cheese** is shown below.

Macaroni Cheese — Ingredients
Water, Wheat, Cheddar Cheese, Rapeseed Oil, Salt, Sugar, Milk Powder, Mustard, Emulsifiers

a) Rapeseed oil is a plant oil. You get it in the same way as olive oil. Tick the box next to the method.

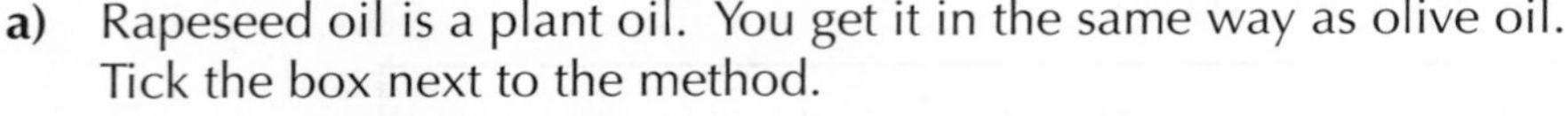

☐ Rapeseed is boiled and then the oil is fractionally distilled

☐ Rapeseed is crushed into a mush and the oil is pressed out.

b) Rapeseed oil is an unsaturated oil. Circle the right words in the sentence.

Rapeseed oil **will / will not** turn bromine water from orange to colourless.

c) Cheddar cheese contains a lot of saturated fat.
Name **one health problem** that too much saturated fat can cause. ....

d) The macaroni cheese contains emulsifiers. Why are emulsifiers added to foods?
Circle the answer.

To stop emulsions from separating out.   To make food taste better.

To make emulsions smell better.

Q4 The Earth's **crust** is broken up into large **chunks**.

a) Fill in the gaps in the sentences with the words below.

tectonic plates	convection currents	evidence

The Earth's surface is made up of .... Wegener discovered .... for this. We think that these chunks move around because of ....

b) Circle the **two** things that can happen where plates meet.

lightening   volcanoes   fossil fuels   earthquakes

Infrared Radiation

Q1 Are these sentences **true** or **false**? Tick the boxes.

		True	False
a)	Infrared radiation is heat.	☐	☐
b)	Hot objects do not emit infrared radiation.	☐	☐
c)	The hotter the object, the more infrared radiation it will emit.	☐	☐
d)	Cold objects emit more radiation than they absorb.	☐	☐

Q2 a) Which object below would **reflect** the most infrared radiation? Circle the right answer.

b) Which object below would **absorb** the most infrared radiation? Circle the right answer.

Q3 Circle the right word in the sentences below.

a) Matt surfaces are **good / bad** at absorbing heat radiation.

b) Shiny surfaces are **good / bad** at reflecting heat radiation.

c) Light coloured surfaces are **good / bad** at absorbing heat radiation.

d) Light coloured surfaces are **good / bad** at emitting heat radiation.

Q4 Will a **solar hot water panel** work better if it is painted **black** or **white**? Circle the right word below and explain your answer.

The panel will work better if it is painted **black / white** because ....

....

Solids, Liquids and Gases

Q1 The pictures below show particles in a **solid**, a **liquid** and a **gas**. Draw lines to match each picture to the correct word.

GAS

LIQUID

SOLID

Q2 Tick the boxes to show if each sentence describes a **solid**, a **liquid** or a **gas**.

	solid	liquid	gas
a) The particles are **far apart** and **not** in a pattern.	☐	☐	☐
b) The particles are **quite close together**, but **don't** make a pattern.	☐	☐	☐
c) The particles are **close together** in a **set pattern**.	☐	☐	☐

Q3 Circle the right words to answer the questions below.

a) Which type of matter has particles with the **most energy**?

Solid **Liquid** **Gas**

b) Which type of matter has the **fastest particles**?

Solid **Liquid** **Gas**

c) Which type of matter has particles that will **only vibrate**?

Solid **Liquid** **Gas**

Conduction

Q1 Are these sentences **true** or **false**? Tick the boxes.

		True	False
a)	Conduction involves energy passing between vibrating particles.	☐	☐
b)	Metals are usually good insulators of heat.	☐	☐
c)	The particles in conductors transfer energy quickly.	☐	☐
d)	The particles in conductors are far apart.	☐	☐

Q2 Complete the sentences below. Use words from the box.

energy good free

Metals are .... conductors of heat.

Metals contain .... electrons.

The electrons bash into other particles, transferring their ....

Q3 **Conductors** have different **properties** to **insulators**.
Fill in the table using the properties in the box below.

One has been done for you.

particles are close together heat transfer is slow can have free electrons
no free electrons particles are far apart heat transfer is quick

CONDUCTOR	INSULATOR
particles are close together	

Convection

Q1 Which tank has the **higher density** of fish? Circle the answer.

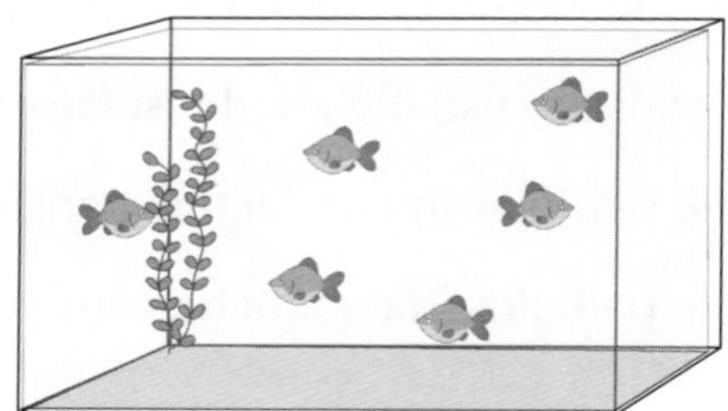

Q2 Are these sentences **true** or **false**? Tick the boxes.

		True	False
a)	The particles in a fluid move more slowly when it is heated.	☐	☐
b)	The density of a fluid goes down when it is heated.	☐	☐
c)	In a hot water tank, the heater coils are at the bottom of the tank.	☐	☐
d)	A denser fluid will rise above a less dense fluid.	☐	☐
e)	Hot fluids rise above cold fluids.	☐	☐
f)	Convection can happen in water, but not in air.	☐	☐

Q3 **Convection** makes water move inside a water heater.

Draw **arrows** on the diagram to show which way the water moves.

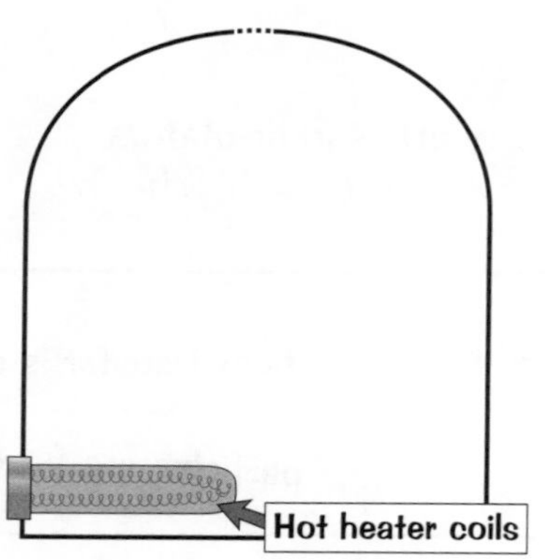

Q4 **Radiators** can heat up a room by **convection**.

Complete the sentences to explain how this works.
Use words from the box.

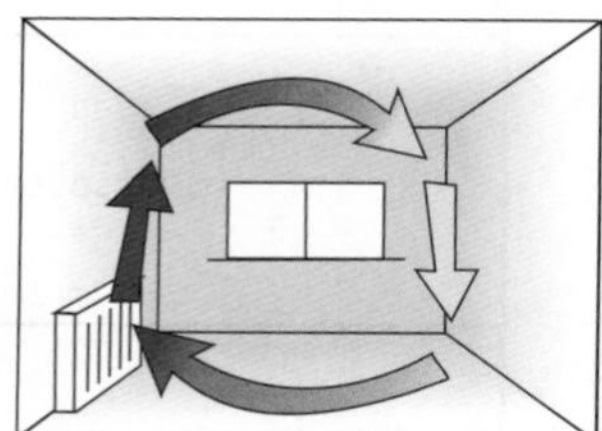

sinks	energy	rises	hot air

The air particles near the radiator are heated up and gain ....

The hot air ....

The cool air ....

The cool air fills the gap left by the ....

Condensation and Evaporation

Q1 Circle the right words in the sentences below.

As a gas cools, the particles in the gas slow down and lose **mass / energy**.

The gas changes into a liquid. This is called **condensation / evaporation**.

Gases often change into a liquid when they hit a **hot / cold** surface.

Q2 Draw lines to match each word to its description.

Condensation	Particles in a liquid escaping to form a gas.
Evaporation	Gases changing to liquids.

Q3 Are these sentences **true** or **false**? Tick the boxes.

		True	False
a)	The particles with the most energy are the least likely to escape from a liquid.	☐	☐
b)	A glass of hot water will evaporate faster than a glass of cold water.	☐	☐
c)	The greater the airflow over a liquid, the more evaporation there will be.	☐	☐
d)	The smaller the surface of the liquid, the more evaporation there will be.	☐	☐
e)	Evaporation makes liquids cool down.	☐	☐

Q4 Tick the box to show which gas will **condense faster** in each pair.

a)	A cold gas	☐	**OR**	☐	A hot gas
b)	A gas that touches a warm surface	☐	**OR**	☐	A gas that touches a cold surface
c)	A gas that touches a small surface	☐	**OR**	☐	A gas that touches a large surface

Rate of Heat Transfer

Q1 **Radiators** are used to **transfer heat** to the air around them.

a) Circle the right words in the sentences below.

> The rate of heat transfer is how much heat energy is passed on in a certain **space / time**.
>
> The bigger the surface area of an object, the **lower / higher** the rate of heat transfer.
>
> Conductors transfer energy **faster / slower** than insulators.
>
> Objects touching a **conductor / insulator** transfer energy faster.

b) The radiators A and B are at the **same temperature** and have the **same surface area**. Which radiator will transfer heat **faster**? Circle the correct answer.

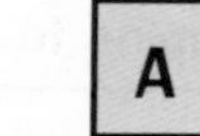

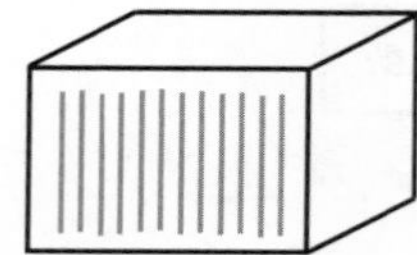

big volume

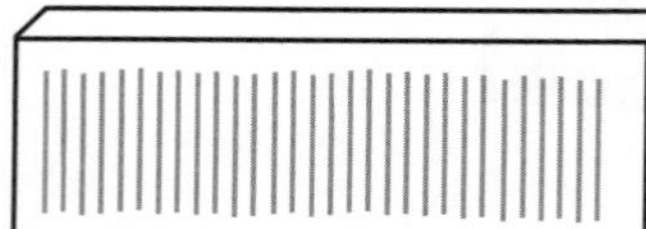

small volume

Q2 The engine below has a **high rate of heat transfer**. Circle all the sentences that explain why.

The engine has a small surface area.

The engine is made from insulating materials.

The engine is made of metal.

The engine has cooling fins.

The engine has a large surface area.

Q3 The flasks A and B contain the same amount of hot water at the same temperature. They are left to cool in **different rooms**.

A — Room at 20 °C

B — Room at 25 °C

Which flask will cool **faster**?
Circle the correct letter below.
Give a reason for your answer.

Flask **A / B** will cool faster because ....

....

Rate of Heat Transfer

Q4 Below is a list of **four** features of a **vacuum flask** that reduce heat transfer. Circle the right word to complete each sentence.

a) A **plastic cap filled with cork** reduces heat transfer by:

conduction radiation convection

b) **Shiny silver walls** reduce heat transfer by:

conduction convection radiation

c) A **vacuum** stops conduction and heat transfer by:

convection radiation

d) **Air** is a good insulator. It reduces heat transfer by:

convection radiation conduction

Plastic cap filled with cork

Shiny silver walls

Vacuum

Air

Q5 The picture shows two different types of fox. One fox lives in a **cold place** and one lives in a **hot desert**.

a) Which fox lives in a **hot desert**?
Circle the correct answer.

Fox A Fox B

Fox A

Fox B

b) How does the **ear size** of the **desert fox** help it to keep cool? Tick the box next to the answer.

☐ The ears have a **small surface area** to **increase** heat loss by radiation.

☐ The ears have a **large surface area** to **reduce** heat loss by radiation.

☐ The ears have a **small surface area** to **reduce** heat loss by radiation.

☐ The ears have a **large surface area** to **increase** heat loss by radiation.

Energy Efficiency in the Home

Q1 Complete the sentences to explain how **insulation** works. Use words from the box.

gaps conduction fibreglass convection

To insulate your loft, put down a thick layer of .... wool.

This reduces heat loss by .... and convection.

To insulate your walls, squirt insulating foam into the .... between the bricks.

This traps pockets of air, which reduces heat loss by ....

Q2 The table below shows information about a hot water tank jacket and loft insulation.

	Hot water tank jacket	**Loft insulation**
Initial Cost	£60	£200
Annual Saving	£15	£100
Payback time = initial cost ÷ annual saving	60 ÷ 15 = 4 years	.... ÷ .... = ... years

a) Complete the table by calculating the **payback time** for **loft insulation**.

b) Which insulation is better value for money? Circle the answer.

Hot water tank jacket Loft insulation

c) Circle the right word in the sentence below.

The more money you save over a period of time, the **more / less** cost-effective the insulation is.

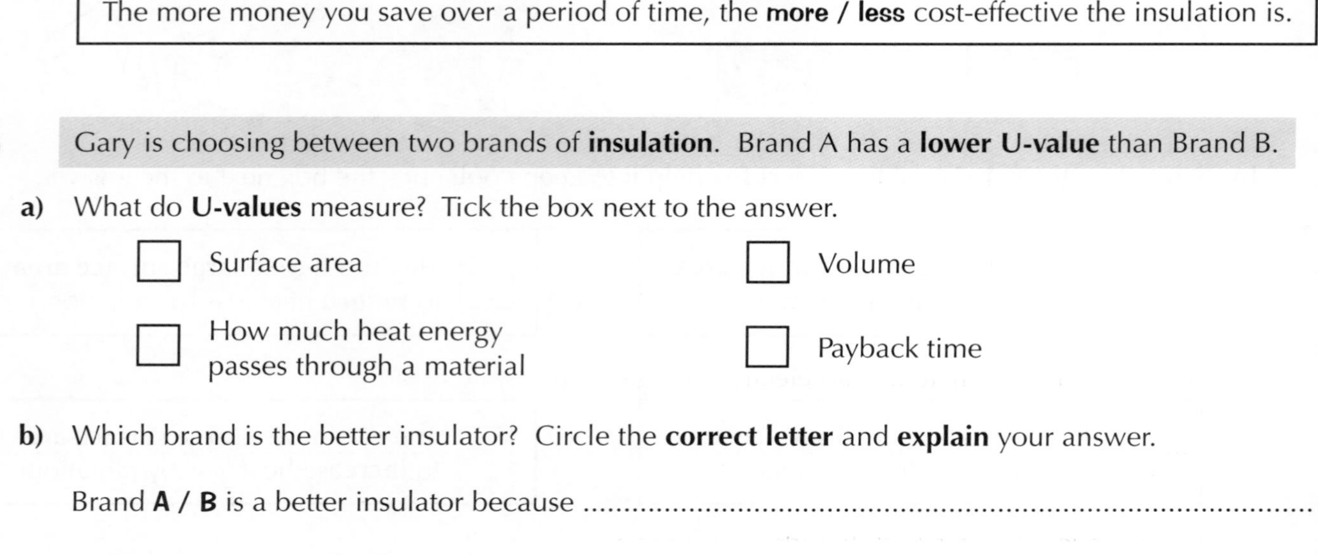

Q3 Gary is choosing between two brands of **insulation**. Brand A has a **lower U-value** than Brand B.

a) What do **U-values** measure? Tick the box next to the answer.

- ☐ Surface area
- ☐ Volume
- ☐ How much heat energy passes through a material
- ☐ Payback time

b) Which brand is the better insulator? Circle the **correct letter** and **explain** your answer.

Brand **A / B** is a better insulator because ....

....

Specific Heat Capacity

Q1 What is **specific heat capacity**? Circle the answer.

A — The difference in temperature between something and the air around it.

B — The amount of energy needed to raise the temperature of 1 kg of something by 1 °C.

C — The amount of energy needed to melt 1 kg of something.

Example: Water has a specific heat capacity of **4.2 J/kg°C**. Calculate the energy needed to raise the temperature of **1 kg** of water by **20 °C**.

Write out the specific heat capacity equation. → $E = m \times c \times \theta$

$E = 1\text{ kg} \times 4200\text{ J/kg°C} \times 20\text{ °C} = 84\,000\text{ J}$ ← Don't forget to write the correct units.

Plug the numbers in.

Work out the answer with a calculator.

Q2 **Mercury** has a specific heat capacity of **139 J/kg°C**.

27 kg of mercury cools by **50 °C**. How much **energy** is released?
Complete the equation below to work it out.

Energy = ... × 139 × .... = ... J

Q3 Answer the questions about **storing heat**. Use the words in the boxes below.

water | oil | brick | energy

a) If a material has a **high heat capacity**, what can it **store** lots of?

....

b) What **liquid** is used in the heaters in **most** houses?

....

c) Some electric storage heaters store heat in **concrete**.
What **other** solid material can electric storage heaters store heat in?

....

d) Complete the sentence:
Even though they are both liquids, water has a higher heat capacity than ....

Energy Transfer

Q1 Circle the right **types of energy** to answer the questions below.

a) Bruce eats breakfast. What type of energy is in his **food**?

Nuclear Sound Chemical

b) Bruce climbs a tree. What type of energy does he have **at the top of the tree**?

Gravitational Potential Electrical Elastic Potential

c) Bruce goes for a drive in a car. What type of energy does he have when **moving**?

Light Kinetic Nuclear

d) Bruce sings a song. What kind of energy does he give out?

Chemical Gravitational Potential Sound

Q2 Are these sentences **true** or **false**? Tick the boxes.

	True	False
a) Energy can be created.	☐	☐
b) Energy can be destroyed.	☐	☐
c) Energy can be transferred from one form to another.	☐	☐
d) Energy is always conserved.	☐	☐

Q3 Complete the following **energy transfer diagrams**. One has been done for you.

Solar Panel

Light Energy → Electrical Energy

a) **Gas Cooker**

.... Energy → Heat Energy + Light Energy

b) **Electric Buzzer**

Electrical Energy → .... Energy + Heat Energy

c) **Television screen**

Electrical Energy → .... Energy + ... Energy

Efficiency of Machines

Example: The total energy into a washing machine is **10 000 J**. The useful energy out is **2000 J**. Calculate its **efficiency**.

Write out the equation for efficiency. → **Efficiency = Useful energy out ÷ Total energy in**

Efficiency = 2000 ÷ 10 000 = 0.2

Plug the numbers in.

Work out the answer with a calculator.

Multiply by 100 to get the answer as a percentage (%).

Q1 Complete the sentences below. Use words from the box.

heat	spreads	energy	wasted

Appliances change .... from one form to another.

Some of the energy put in is transferred to useful forms.

The energy that is not transferred to useful forms is ....

Most energy that is wasted is wasted as ....

This energy .... out so it can't be used again.

Q2 The diagram shows energy going in and out of a light bulb. Complete the sentences about the light bulb.

a) The **total energy in** is .... J

b) The **useful energy out** is .... J

c) The amount of energy **wasted** is .... J

Wasted energy = Total energy − Useful energy

Q3 Work out the **efficiency** of each appliance below as a **decimal**. Fill in the table with each answer.

Appliance	Total Energy In (J)	Useful Energy Out (J)	Efficiency
1	2000	1000	
2	4000	3000	
3	4000	1000	

Efficiency of Machines

Q4 Some cars have **heat exchangers**.

Circle the right words in the sentences below.

A heat exchanger makes use of **chemical / wasted** energy.

In cars, they use energy from the hot **engine / lights**.

The heat is used to warm **air / water**.

This can then be used to keep the passengers **cool / warm**.

Q5 The table below shows information on **low-energy** and **ordinary** light bulbs:

	Low-energy bulb	Ordinary bulb
Cost to buy	£3.00	£0.50
Cost to use for one year	£1.00	£4.00

Use the table to help you answer the following questions:

a) Which bulb is the **cheapest to buy**?

....

b) Which bulb is the cheapest to use for **1 year**?

....

c) How much money would you save on energy bills every year by swapping an ordinary bulb for a low-energy bulb?

....

d) The equation for **payback time** is:

Payback time = Initial cost ÷ annual saving

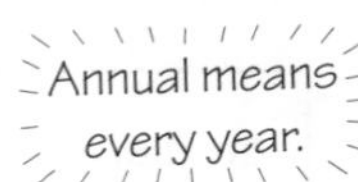

Complete the calculation below to work out the payback time for a low-energy bulb:

Payback time = ... ÷ .... = ... **year(s)**

Sankey Diagrams

Q1 a) What does a **Sankey diagram** show? Tick the answer.

How the temperature changes as something uses energy. ☐

How much of the input energy is changed into different types of energy. ☐

What appliances are used for. ☐

b) Circle the right word in the sentence.

The wider the arrow on a Sankey diagram, the more **energy** / **efficiency** it shows.

c) Which of the arrows in a Sankey diagram is the widest?
Circle the answer.

Useful energy out **Wasted energy** **Input energy**

Q2 The sketch below is a **Sankey diagram** for a blender.

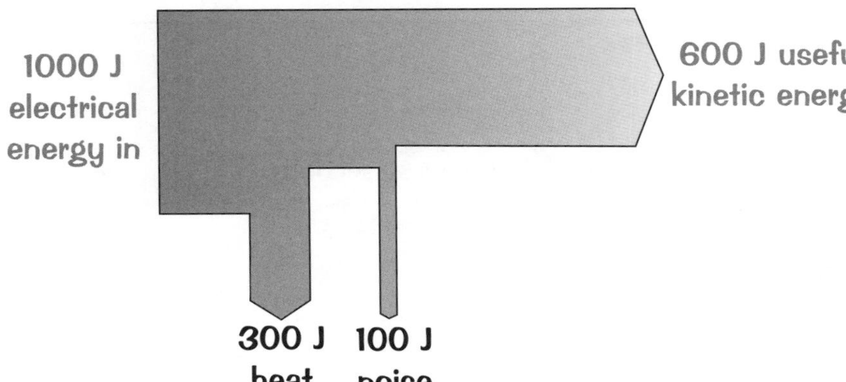

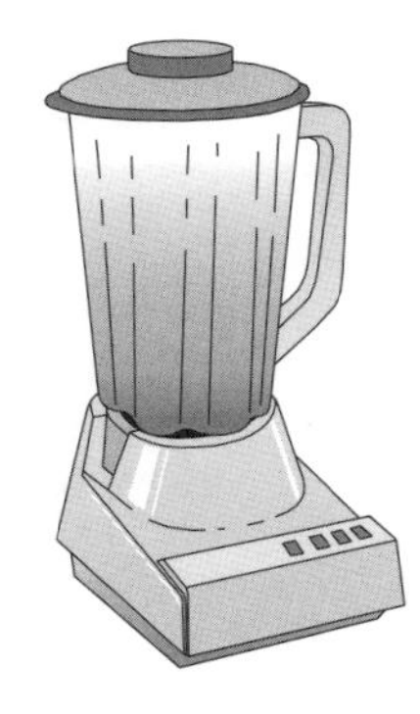

a) How is **most** of the energy **wasted**? Circle the answer.

as electrical energy as noise as heat as kinetic energy

b) Use the Sankey diagram to complete the table below.

Input Energy (J)	Useful Energy Out (J)	Wasted Energy (J)
1000	....	....

Electrical Energy

Q1 Complete these sentences on electrical energy. Use words from the list.

power **joules** **electrical**

a) Electrical appliances transfer .... energy into other forms of energy.

b) The amount of energy an electrical appliance transfers depends on how long it's switched on for and its ....

c) Energy transferred can be measured in .... or kilowatt-hours.

Example: A fridge has a power of **0.05 kW**. It is left on for **24 hours**. Calculate the energy transferred to the fridge in kilowatt-hours.

Write out the equation for energy transferred. → **E = P × t**

E = 0.05 kW × 24 hours = 1.2 kWh ← *Don't forget to write the correct units.*

Plug the numbers in.

Work out the answer with a calculator.

Q2 An appliance with a power of **45 W** is left on for **30 seconds**. How much energy is transferred? Tick the box.

75 J ☐ 1350 J ☐

1.5 J ☐ 0.67 J ☐

You'll need to use energy transferred = power × time.

Q3 Boris puts his **2 kW** electric heater on for **3 hours**.

Calculate how much energy is transferred in kilowatt-hours.

....

....

....

The Cost of Electricity

Example: Electricity costs **14p** per kWh. How much does it cost to use **10 kWh**?

Write out the equation for total cost. → **total cost = energy transferred × price per kWh**

Plug the numbers in. → **total cost = 10 kWh × 14p = 140p** ← Work out the answer with a calculator.

100p = £1.00 so 140p = £1.40 ← Divide by 100 to get the answer in £.

Q1 Helen's electricity costs **12p per kWh**.
How much would it cost her to use **20 kWh**? Tick the box.

☐ £2.40 ☐ 24p ☐ 0.6p

Q2 Tina leaves a lamp on all night. The total energy transferred is **0.5 kWh**.
Her electricity costs **15p** per kWh.

a) Work out how much it costs to leave the lamp on all night.

....

Cost = ... p

b) The cost of electricity is going up to **17p** per kWh.
What will be the new cost of leaving the lamp on all night? Circle the answer.

30p **8.5p** **8p** **34p**

Q3 Jim wants to work out how much electricity he uses in a week.

He takes one meter reading at the start of the week and one at the end. The meters are shown below.

1 3 5 9 2 kWh	1 3 6 7 7 kWh
Start of week	**End of week**

a) How much electricity did Jim use during the week?

.... kWh

b) Jim's electricity costs **11p** per kWh.
How much would it cost, in £, for this week?

Remember, 100p = £1.00.
So to change p to £, divide by 100.

....

Choosing Electrical Appliances

Q1 Electricity has lots of important uses.

Draw lines to match up each use of electricity with its description. One has been done for you.

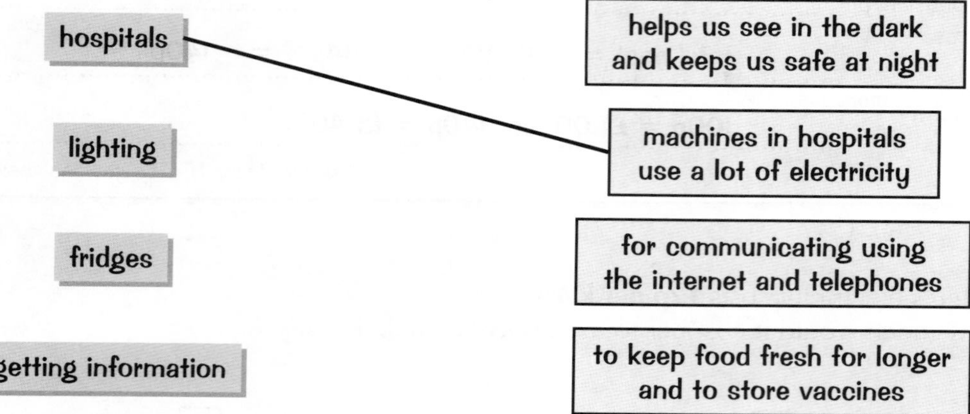

Q2 Why might you take a **wind-up radio** on a camping trip rather than a **mains-powered radio**? Tick **two** boxes.

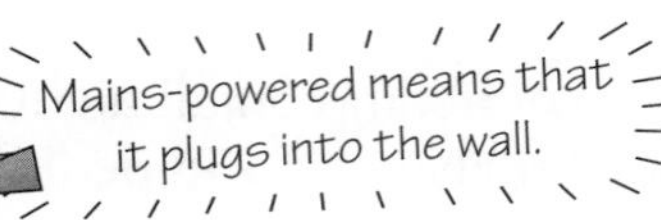

There might not be an electricity supply. ☐

A wind-up radio will need winding up regularly. ☐

Wind-up radios don't have wires that might get in the way. ☐

Q3 Cheryl wants to buy a hair dryer to take on **holiday**. She has to choose between hair dryers **A** and **B**.

Hair dryer A:
Cost: £25.00
Power: 2.2 kW
Weight: 130 g
Special features: 5 speeds and temperature control

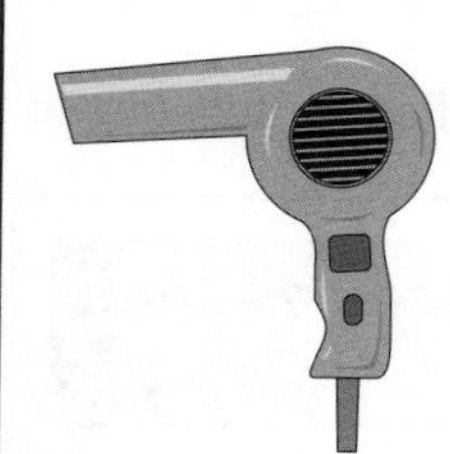

Hair dryer B:
Cost: £12.99
Power: 1.2 kW
Weight: 95 g
Special features: Handle folds away

a) Give **one** reason why Cheryl might choose hair dryer **A**.

....

b) Give **one** reason why Cheryl might choose hair dryer **B**.

....

Mixed Questions — Physics 1a

Q1 Paul is cooking some sausages under the **grill**.

a) How is **heat transferred** from the grill to the sausages?
Circle the answer.

conduction **convection** **radiation**

b) Paul lines his grill pan with **shiny foil**. How does this **help him** to grill his sausages?
Circle the answer.

A — The shiny surface absorbs the heat conducted from the grill.

B — The shiny surface helps the heat flow by convection.

C — The shiny surface reflects the heat radiation back on to the sausages.

c) Draw lines to match the type of heat transfer to its description.

Conduction	Vibrating particles pass on energy to the particles next to them.
Convection	Particles with more energy move from a hot place to a cooler one.

d) Paul uses **0.5 kWh** of electricity to cook the meal. Electricity costs Paul **14p** per kWh.
How much does it cost Paul for the electricity to cook the meal? Circle the answer.

7p **28p** **14.5p**

Q2 Humans and animals have ways of coping with **low temperatures**.

a) Circle the right words in the sentences below.

Air is a very good **conductor / insulator**.

When you get cold, your body hairs **stand up / lie flat**.

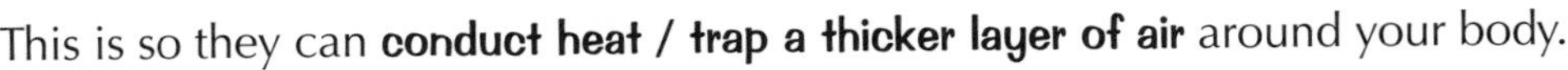

This is so they can **conduct heat / trap a thicker layer of air** around your body.

This reduces the heat lost by **conduction / radiation**.

b) Give **two** ways that heat loss from houses can be **reduced**.

1. ....

2. ....

Mixed Questions — Physics 1a

Q3 A power station burns coal.

a) What **type** of energy is in the **coal**?
Circle the answer.

Nuclear   Chemical   Electrical   Light

b) In the power station, for every **1000 J** of energy in, **600 J** are wasted.
Complete the calculations to find the **efficiency** of the power station.

Useful energy out = 1000 J – 600 J = ... J

Efficiency = Useful energy out ÷ Total energy in

Efficiency = ... ÷ ....

Efficiency = ...

Q4 Jonny heats his house by burning coal. He finds out about different ways of heating his house and writes the information down in the table below.

Heating	Annual Saving (£)	Initial Cost (£)	Payback time (years) = Initial Cost ÷ Annual Saving
Oil heaters	20	100	100 ÷ 20 = **5**
Water central heating	100	600	600 ÷ 100 = ...
Storage heaters	30	120	.... ÷ .... = ...

a) Calculate the payback times to complete the table.

b) Which heating system has the **shortest payback time**?

....

c) Oil has a **specific heat capacity** of **2500 J/kg°C**.
Calculate the energy stored by **10 kg** of oil when heated by **20 °C**.
Use the equation below to help you.

Energy = Mass × Specific Heat Capacity × Temperature Change

Energy = ... × 2500 × .... = ... J

Energy Sources & Power Stations

Q1 Energy sources can be **renewable** or **non-renewable**.

a) Draw lines to match each word with its meaning.

Non-renewable	will never run out
Renewable	will run out one day

b) Circle the energy sources below that are **non-renewable**. Circle **two** answers.

Coal Wind Geothermal Nuclear

Q2 a) Write the numbers 1–4 in the boxes to put the sentences in the **right order**. One has been done for you.

☐ The steam turns a turbine.

☐ The generator makes electricity.

1 Fuel is burnt to heat water to make steam.

☐ The turbine turns a generator.

b) Name **three** fossil fuels.

1. ....

2. ....

3. ....

Q3 Use the words to fill in the gaps in the sentences.

plutonium	electricity	steam	turbine	fission

Nuclear power stations use a reaction called nuclear ....

This reaction is used to heat water to make ....

This then turns a ...., which is used to drive a generator.

The generator makes ....

The fuels used for this reaction are uranium and ....

Renewable Energy Sources (1)

Q1 a) Circle the energy sources that are **renewable**. Circle **four** answers.

Oil Tides Gas

Waves Solar Biofuels

b) Give **one advantage** of using renewable energy sources.

....

Q2 Tick the box next to the **disadvantage** of using renewable energy sources.

- ☐ The waste they produce is very dangerous.
- ☐ They will never run out.
- ☐ They don't give us as much energy as non-renewable sources.

Q3 Are these sentences **true** or **false**? Tick the boxes.

		True	False
a)	Wind turbines only work when it's windy.	☐	☐
b)	Wind turbines can harm wildlife like birds.	☐	☐
c)	Wind turbines can only be used to generate a large amount of power.	☐	☐
d)	Wind turbines can spoil the view.	☐	☐

Q4 Circle the right words in the sentences below.

a) The blades of a wind turbine turn the **operator** / **generator** inside. This makes electricity.

b) Wind turbines don't make any **harmful gases** / **noise**.

c) Wind turbines are **cheap** / **expensive** to run.

d) Wind turbines **cost a lot** / **don't cost much** to build.

Renewable Energy Sources (2)

Q1 Using **solar cells** has advantages and disadvantages.
Put the sentences about solar cells in the table below.

They are cheap to run.

They don't make any harmful gases.

They cost a lot to make.

They only work during the day.

They're useful in places that don't have mains electricity.

Advantages of using Solar Cells	Disadvantages of using Solar Cells

Q2 a) Circle the words to complete the sentence below.

The **National Grid / National Arena** is the name given to all the cables and other equipment that carry electricity around the country.

b) Complete the sentences below using words from the box.

difficult	expensive	electricity	money

Not everything that makes .... can be connected to the National Grid. It might be too .... to connect things that only make small amounts of electricity. It might be too .... to connect things in remote locations.

Renewable Energy Sources (3)

Q1 Draw lines to link the parts of the sentences together.

Pumped storage stations...

Hydroelectric power stations...

...use rainwater trapped behind a dam.

...store energy which has already been generated.

Q2 Circle the right words in the sentences.

Hydroelectric power uses **falling** / **swirling** water to make electricity.

Water is trapped by a **bridge** / **dam**.

When electricity is needed, the water is let out through a **generator** / **turbine**.

This turns a **generator** / **turbine** to make electricity.

Q3 a) Number the steps below 1–3 to show how **pumped storage** works. One has been done for you.

☐ The water is stored high up.

1 Spare electricity is used to pump water up to a high place.

☐ The water is released when lots of electricity is needed.

b) Choose from the words in the box to complete the sentence below.

demand	**profit**	**energy**

Pumped storage lets you **match** supply and ....

Q4 Give **two advantages** of using hydroelectric power.

1. ....

....

2. ....

....

Renewable Energy Sources (4)

Q1 a) Complete the sentences about **tidal power**. Use words from the box.

tides	generators	turbines

Tidal power uses .... to make electricity.

As the tide flows in and out it turns ....

The turbines turn .... to make electricity.

Use each word once.

b) Circle the right word in the sentence below.

Tidal power stations are **cheap / expensive** to run.

c) Give **one disadvantage** of using tidal power stations.

....

Q2 **Wave power** can be very useful around islands.

a) Add the labels to the diagram by writing the correct letters in the boxes.

A — water wave moves in

B — turbine turns generator to make electricity

C — air turns turbine

D — air is forced out

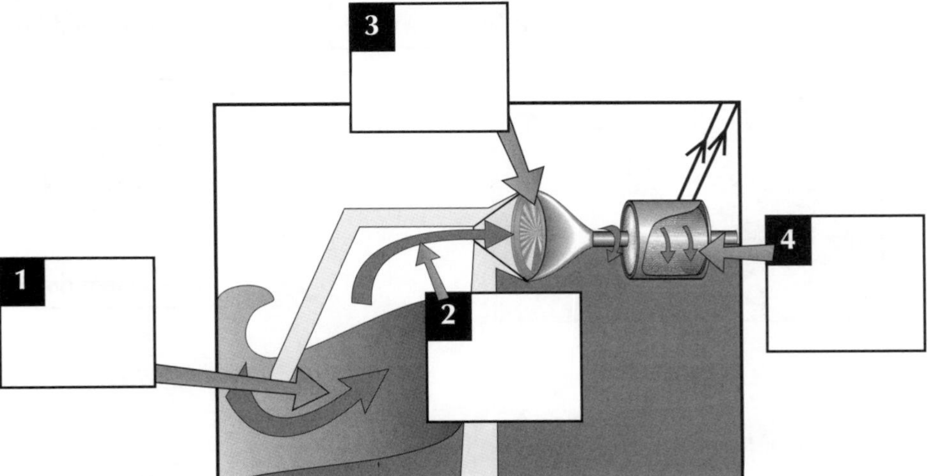

b) Give **one** possible **problem** of using wave power.

....

Renewable Energy Sources (5)

Q1 Use the words to fill in the gaps in the sentences.

electricity **turbine** **generator** **water**

Biofuels are used to make ....

Biofuels are burnt to heat .... to make steam.

This steam is used to drive a ....

This then turns a ....

Q2 Why are biofuels a **renewable** source of energy? Circle the answer.

They don't cause any pollution.

They won't run out.

They depend on the weather.

They are cheap to make.

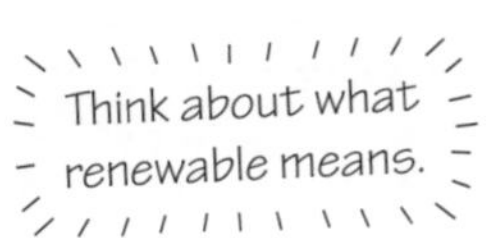

Bernard had just found out biofuels were made from plants.

Q3 Add the labels to the diagram by writing the correct letters in the boxes.

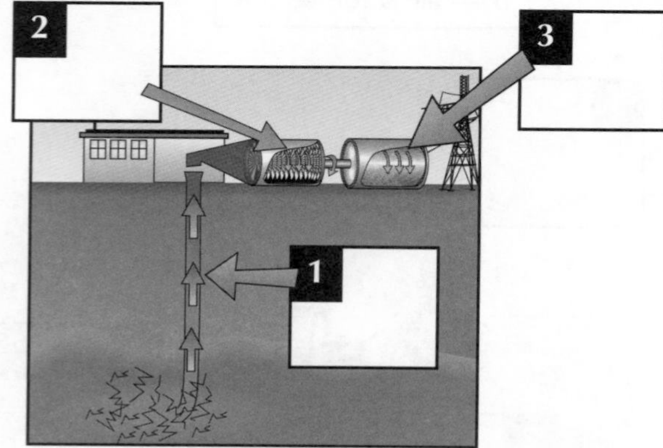

A — steam and hot water rises to the surface of the ground

B — turbines turn a generator to make electricity

C — steam drives a turbine

Q4 Are these sentences **true** or **false**? Tick the boxes.

		True	False
a)	It doesn't cost a lot to build geothermal power stations.	☐	☐
b)	It is possible to use geothermal energy everywhere in the world.	☐	☐
c)	No harmful gases are made when using geothermal energy.	☐	☐

Energy Sources and the Environment

Q1 Draw lines to match up each problem with something that causes it. One has been done for you.

Problem	Cause
Harm to the sea and animals	Burning fossil fuels
Carbon dioxide is given out	Coal mining
Dangerous waste is made	Oil spills
The view is spoilt	Using nuclear power

Q2 a) Circle the right words in the sentences below.

Carbon capture and storage (CCS) is used to catch carbon dioxide from **power stations** / **petrol stations**.

This helps to **increase** / **decrease** the amount of carbon dioxide in the air.

This helps **increase** / **decrease** global warming.

b) Where can the captured carbon dioxide be **stored**? Tick the box.

- [ ] lead boxes
- [ ] holes under the North Sea where oil and gas used to be
- [ ] carbon dioxide pools in Antarctica
- [ ] large warehouses

carbon dioxide

Q3 Are these sentences **true** or **false**? Tick the boxes.

		True	False
a)	Forests are sometimes chopped down to make room to grow biofuels.	☐	☐
b)	Biofuels increase the amount of carbon dioxide in the air.	☐	☐
c)	Plants are used to make biofuels.	☐	☐
d)	Chopping down trees to grow biofuels means that some animals lose their homes.	☐	☐

Comparison of Energy Sources

Q1 Which type of power station has the **shortest start-up time**? Circle the answer.

Coal power stations

Oil power stations

Gas power stations

Q2 Circle the right words in the sentences below.

a) Renewable energy power stations are **expensive** / **cheap** to build.

b) Nuclear reactors and hydroelectric dams cost the **most** / **least** to build.

c) Renewable energy power stations are **expensive** / **cheap** to run.

d) A power station usually has to be **near to** / **far away from** the thing it runs on.

Q3 a) Which type of power station is usually the **cheapest** to run? Tick the box.

☐ Renewable energy power stations ☐ Non-renewable energy power stations

b) Why is it cheaper to run this type? Circle the answer.

The fuels used are free.

They make more electricity.

People can be paid less to work in power stations that use this energy source.

Q4 a) Name two types of power stations that can make noise pollution.

1. ....

2. ....

b) Name one type of power station that makes dangerous waste.

....

Comparison of Energy Sources

Q5 It can cost a lot of money to **decommission** a power station.

a) What does **decommissioning** a power station mean? Circle the answer.

Fixing it. Taking it apart. Building it.

b) Which type of power station takes the **longest time** to decommission? Tick the box.

☐ Coal-fired power stations

☐ Hydroelectric power stations

☐ Nuclear power stations

Q6 Draw lines to match up the **type** of power station with its **location**.

Type of power station	Location
geothermal	away from people and near water
hydroelectric	hilly, rainy places
nuclear	near a coal mine
coal	volcanic places

Q7 Complete the table to give **one disadvantage** of each energy source. One has been done for you.

Energy Source	Disadvantage
Gas	Causes pollution.
Nuclear	
Wind	
Hydroelectric	

Electricity and the National Grid

Q1 Tick the boxes to answer these questions on **overhead** and **underground cables**. One has been done for you.

	Overhead Cables	Underground Cables
Which costs more to set up?		✓
Which are easier to fix?		
Which are more likely to be damaged by the weather?		
Which are easier to set up?		

Q2 Label the diagram of the National Grid using the words in the box.

pylons   step-up transformer   power station   step-down transformer

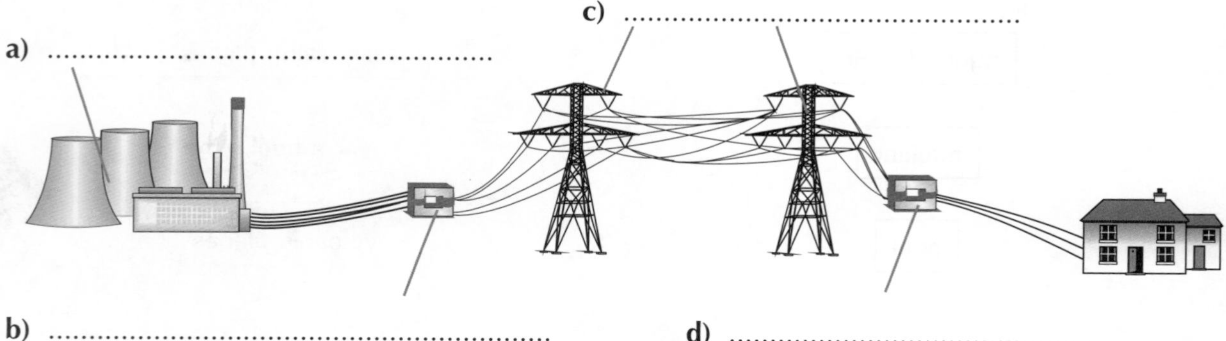

Q3 Circle the right words in the sentences below.

Electricity travels through the National Grid at a **high** / **low** voltage and at a low current. This helps to **increase** / **decrease** the energy that is lost as the electricity travels through the cables.

Q4 Our energy demands are increasing. To meet these demands, what could we do? Tick **two** boxes.

'Demands are increasing' just means we want more and more.

☐ Increase the energy given to the National Grid.

☐ Decrease the energy given to the National Grid.

☐ Increase our energy demands.

☐ Reduce our energy demands.

Wave Basics

Q1 Circle the right word in the sentence below.

Waves transfer **energy / matter** from one place to another.

Q2 a) Draw lines to match each wave with its name.

Transverse

Longitudinal

b) In which direction are the vibrations in a **longitudinal** wave? Tick one box.

☐ Perpendicular (at 90°) to the direction the wave is travelling.

☐ Parallel to the direction (in the same direction as) the wave is travelling.

Q3 Draw lines to match the words with their descriptions.

Wavelength	The number of full waves that pass a point per second.
Frequency	The distance from the rest position to a crest or a trough.
Amplitude	The length of one full wave.

Q4 Tick the sentences below that are true.

☐ In transverse waves the vibrations are at 90° to the direction that energy is transferred.

☐ Light waves are transverse waves.

☐ Sound waves are transverse waves.

☐ In transverse waves the vibrations are along the same direction that energy is transferred.

☐ Transverse waves show areas of compression and rarefaction.

Wave Basics

Q5 Label this diagram of a wave by adding letters to the boxes.

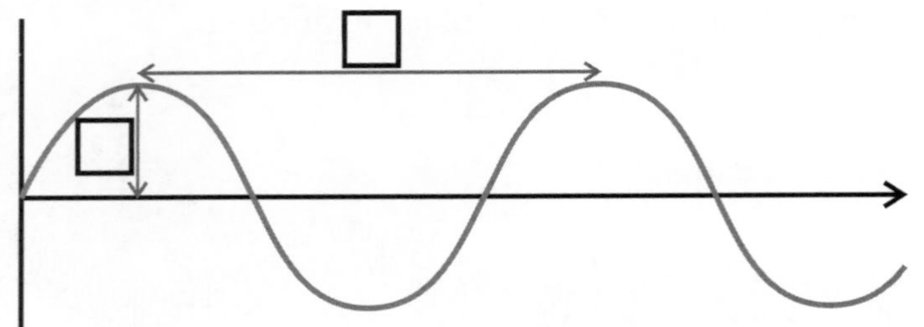

A — wavelength

B — amplitude

Example: A wave has a wavelength of **2 m** and a frequency of **125 Hz**. Calculate the **speed** of the wave. Give the correct units in your answer.

v = f × λ = frequency × wavelength ← Write out the equation for wave speed. You can find it on the equations sheet.

v = 125 Hz × 2 m = 250 m/s ← Don't forget to write the correct units.

Plug the numbers in.

Work out the answer with a calculator.

Q6 A **sound wave** has a wavelength of **4 m** and a frequency of **85 Hz**.

Calculate the **speed** of the sound wave. Give the correct unit in your answer.

Have a look at the example above to help you.

....

....

Q7 A **water wave** has a frequency of **2.5 Hz** and a wavelength of **1 m**.

What is the **speed** of the water wave? Tick one box.

2.5 m/s	☐	3.5 m/s	☐
0.4 m/s	☐	2.5 Hz	☐

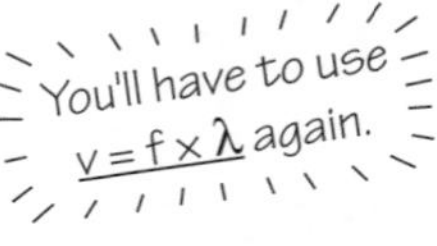

Q8 A radio wave has a frequency of **200 000 Hz**. It has a wavelength of **1500 m**.

Calculate the **speed** of the wave. Give the correct unit in your answer.

....

....

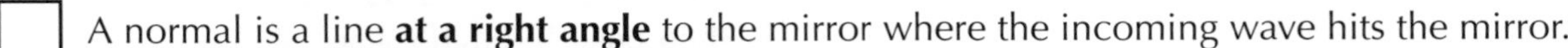

Wave Properties

Q1 A **normal** is used when drawing ray diagrams.

a) What is a normal? Tick **one** box.

☐ A normal is a line **at a right angle** to the mirror where the incoming wave hits the mirror.

☐ A normal is a line **parallel** to the mirror where the incoming wave hits the mirror.

b) The diagram below shows a light wave being reflected by a mirror.

Label the diagram using the words below.

normal **angle of incidence** **angle of reflection**

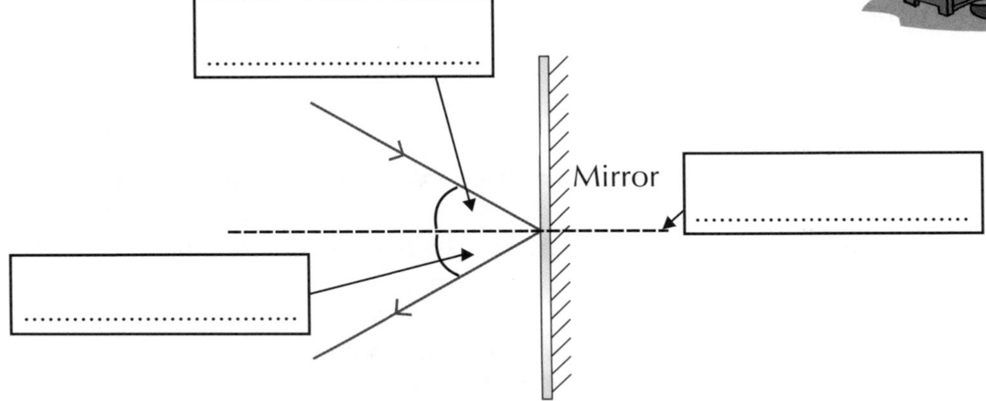

c) Complete the sentence below using words from the list.

bigger than **smaller than** **the same as**

The angle of incidence is always .... the angle of reflection.

Q2 The diagram below shows a pencil being reflected in a **mirror**.

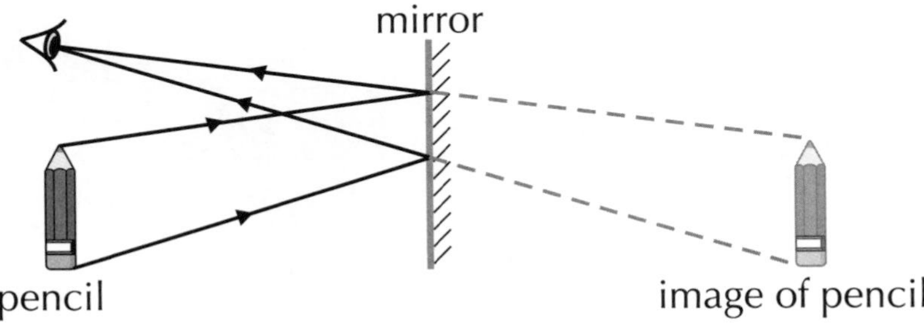

Circle the right words in the sentences below.

a) The image of the pencil in the mirror is a **virtual** / **real** image.

b) The image of the pencil is laterally inverted and **upside down** / **upright**.

Refraction and Diffraction

Q1 Draw lines to match each word with what it means.

Refraction

When waves spread out as they pass through a gap.

When waves change direction as they move from one material to another.

Q2 Circle the right words in the sentences.

Electricity / **Waves** spread out as they pass through a gap.

How much a wave spreads out depends on the **size** / **shape** of the gap.

The waves spread out the **most** / **least** when the wavelength of the wave is the same size as the gap.

The waves spread out the **most** / **least** when the gap is much larger than the wavelength of the wave.

Q3 Diagrams A and B show waves travelling between **two different materials**.

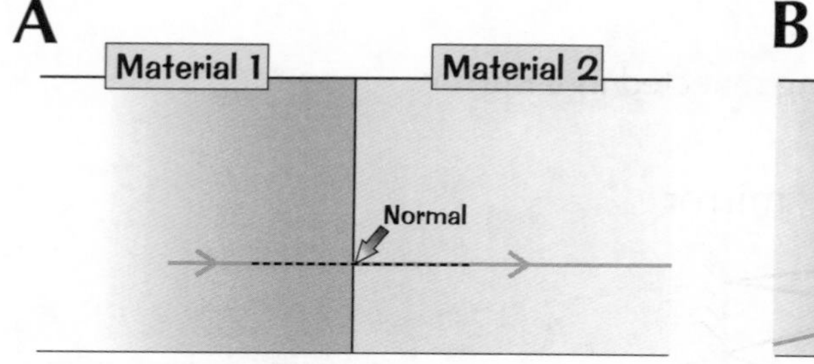

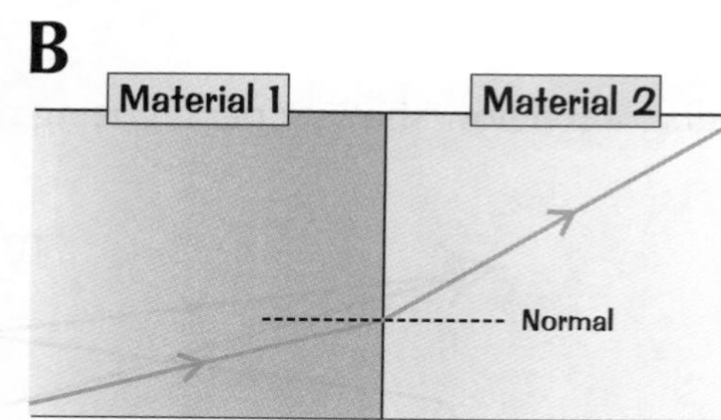

a) Which diagram shows the waves being **refracted**? ....

b) Refraction **doesn't** happen in the other diagram. Why not?

....

....

Electromagnetic Waves and Communication

Q1 a) Complete the electromagnetic spectrum using words from the box.

ultraviolet	visible light	infrared	microwaves	X-rays

radio waves						gamma rays
						Radioactive

LONG wavelength → **SHORT** wavelength

b) Which type of electromagnetic radiation has the **highest energy**?

....

c) Which type of electromagnetic radiation has the **lowest frequency**?

....

Q2 Are these sentences true or false? Tick the boxes.

		True	False
a)	Visible light travels faster than X-rays in a vacuum.	☐	☐
b)	Radio waves have the shortest wavelength of all electromagnetic waves.	☐	☐
c)	All electromagnetic waves can travel through space.	☐	☐
d)	Gamma rays have a higher frequency than radio waves.	☐	☐

Q3 Circle the right words to complete the sentences below.

Radio waves with **short** / **long** wavelengths reflect off the Earth's atmosphere.

They can travel **short** / **long** distances.

Radio waves with **short** / **long** wavelengths can diffract around the Earth.

Electromagnetic Waves and Their Uses

Q1 Use the words to fill in the gaps in the sentences.

image film light

Cameras use visible .... to take photographs.

Cameras focus light on a .... or a sensor at the back of the camera.

This records a(n) ....

Q2 Draw lines to match each type of electromagnetic wave with its use.

microwaves	remote controls
infrared	photography
visible light	mobile phones

Q3 Circle the correct words in the sentences below.

Infrared waves / Microwaves are used to send satellite TV signals. The signal is sent from a **transmitter / receiver** into space. The signal is picked up by a satellite.

The satellite sends the signal back to Earth in **the same / a different** direction.

The signal is picked up by a **satellite dish / radio aerial** on the ground.

Q4 Some people think that using a mobile phone a lot is **dangerous**. Why do they think it's dangerous?

Think about what waves are used to send mobile phone signals.

....

....

Sound Waves

Q1 a) Which of the sentences below is **true**? Tick one box.

- [ ] Sound waves are not understood by scientists.
- [ ] Sound waves pick up vibrations as they travel.
- [ ] Sound waves cause vibrations in the material they travel in.
- [ ] Sound waves help you to see faraway objects.

b) What type of wave is a sound wave? Circle the answer.

transverse   longitudinal

c) Why **can't** sound waves travel in space? Tick the answer.

- [ ] There are no particles.
- [ ] They don't have enough energy.
- [ ] There's not enough room.

Q2 Use the words below to fill in the gaps in the sentences.

quiet   **high**   **low**   **vibrate**   **loud**

A sound wave makes air molecules ....

High frequency sound waves sound .... pitched.

Low frequency sound waves sound .... pitched.

A high amplitude makes a .... sound.

A low amplitude makes a .... sound.

Q3 What is an echo? Circle the answer.

A reflected sound wave.   **A diffracted sound wave.**   **A refracted sound wave.**

The Doppler Effect and Red-shift

Q1 Use the words to fill in the gaps in the sentences.

red-shifted **longer** **shorter** **blue-shifted** **away**

The wavelength of light from distant galaxies is .... than it should be.

This is because the galaxies are moving .... from us.

We say that the light has been ....

You don't have to use all the words.

Q2 Circle the right words in the sentences below.

The further away a galaxy is, the **more** / **less** the light is red-shifted.

So distant galaxies are moving away **slower** / **faster** than nearer ones.

This is evidence that the Universe is getting **smaller** / **bigger**.

Q3 The wavelength and frequency of a wave seem to change if the **wave source** is moving.

a) What is this **effect** called?

A wave source is a thing that waves are coming from.

....

b) What types of wave can this effect happen to? Tick the boxes.

☐ light waves ☐ sound waves ☐ water waves ☐ death rays ☐ microwaves

c) If a wave source is travelling towards you, what happens to the **frequency**? Circle the answer.

It seems to increase. It seems to decrease.

d) If a wave source is travelling towards you, what happens to the **wavelength**? Circle the answer.

It seems to increase. It seems to decrease.

How the Universe Started

Q1 Write the numbers 1–4 in the boxes to put the sentences in the **right order**. One has been done for you.

- [ ] There was a big explosion.
- [1] Everything in the Universe was squashed into a very small point.
- [ ] The Universe started expanding.
- [ ] The Universe is still expanding now.

Q2 What is **cosmic microwave background radiation**? Tick one box.

- It's a type of radiation that is made in nuclear reactors. ☐
- It's a type of radiation that is made in the core of the Earth. ☐
- It's a type of radiation that fills the Universe. ☐

Q3 Are these sentences **true** or **false**? Tick the boxes.

		True	False
a)	Cosmic microwave background radiation is mostly made up of radio waves.	☐	☐
b)	The Big Bang theory is the only theory that can explain cosmic microwave background radiation.	☐	☐
c)	The cosmic microwave background radiation was around shortly after the beginning of the Universe.	☐	☐

Q4 What fact **can't** the Big Bang theory explain? Circle the answer.

The galaxies are all moving away from us.

The galaxies that are furthest away are moving the quickest.

The Universe is getting bigger.

The Universe's expansion is speeding up.

Mixed Questions — Physics 1b

Q1 a) What type of electromagnetic wave does a remote control use?

....

b) Jake can change TV channel by pointing the remote control at a mirror.
The diagram below shows the path of the wave from the remote control to the TV.
Complete the diagram by using words from the box.

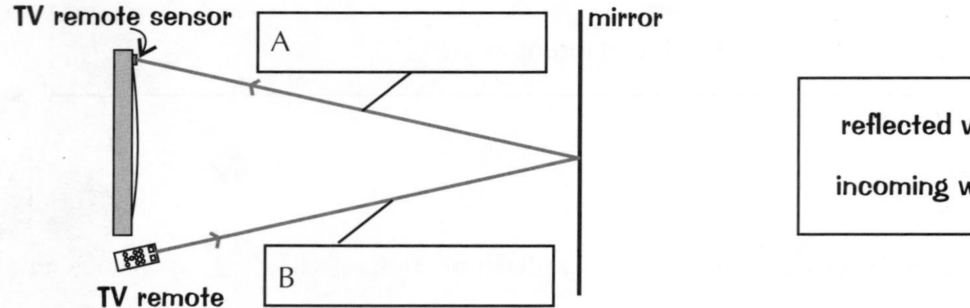

reflected wave

incoming wave

c) What property of waves does the diagram in **b)** show? Circle the correct answer.

reflection **refraction** **diffraction**

Q2 A council are talking about plans to build a new gas power station.

a) This is a diagram of a gas power station. Use the words to fill in the gaps in the labels.

steam **generator** **turbine** **electricity**

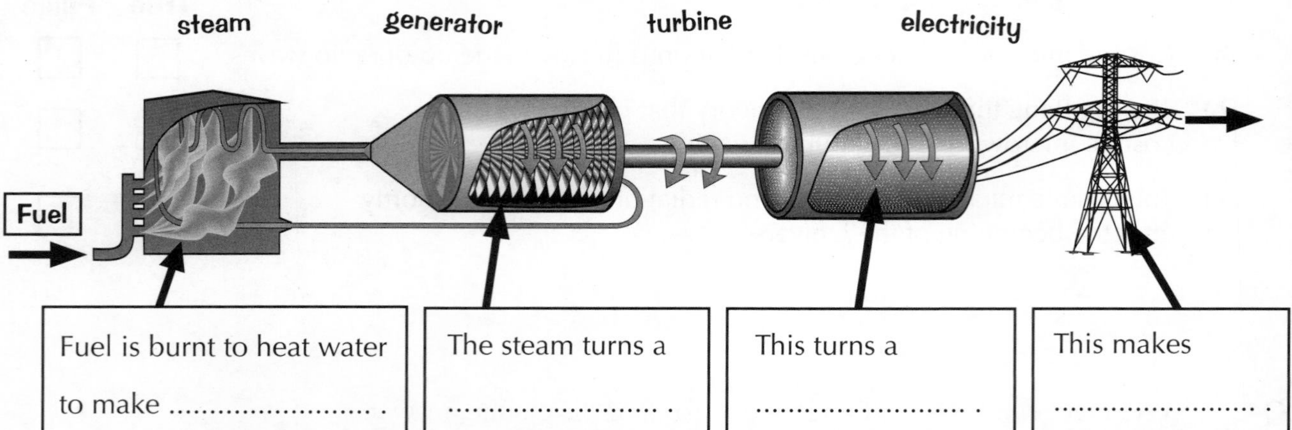

Fuel is burnt to heat water to make	The steam turns a	This turns a	This makes ....

b) Is gas a renewable or non-renewable energy source? Circle the answer.

renewable **non-renewable**

Renewable means it won't run out.

c) Give **one** advantage of **gas power stations**.

....